GINGER

Old Home Remedies
& Many Other Uses

GINGER

Old Home Remedies & Many Other Uses

Margaret Briggs

Abbeydale Press

ISBN 978-1-86147-241-0

1 3 5 7 9 10 8 6 4 2

Published by Abbeydale Press
an imprint of Bookmart Ltd
Registered number 2372865
Trading as Bookmart Ltd
Blaby Road, Wigston, Leicester
LE18 4SE, England

Produced by Omnipress Limited, UK
Illustrations by Tegan Sharrard
Cover design by Omnipress Limited, UK

Printed in Dubai

ABOUT THE AUTHOR

Margaret Briggs was a teacher for 30 years, working in
Kent, Germany, North Yorkshire and Sussex.

Since leaving teaching she has had more time for
gardening and cooking and has embarked on a second
career as a freelance writer, researcher and editor,
alongside her writer husband, Lol. Several years ago the
couple bought a dilapidated house in south-west France.
The house is now restored and Margaret and Lol divide
their time between Sussex and the Gironde, with two
contrasting gardens to develop.

CONTENTS

Introduction

Over the past couple of years I've become used to the amused expressions on the faces of friends and family as they ask 'And what book are you working on now?' After a writing career that started with vinegar and porridge as subjects, I can see their point. I'm often amused myself by the subjects I'm asked to write about, actually. They always provide, however, plenty of surprises when it comes to filling in gaps in historical, scientific or culinary knowledge, plenty of headaches over stacks of material and how to organise and present it, as well as a good laugh or two along the way: just like some aspects of teaching, really.

When ginger as a subject was first mooted, I was enthusiastic, because I use a lot of ginger in cooking, especially in Indian and oriental-style dishes. Other people came up with the obvious lines about ginger and cockney rhyming slang, or a range of comments about people with ginger hair (red, auburn or strawberry blonde, I mean) being particularly feisty . . . oh, and a particular member of a re-formed girl band being 'spicy'. It's probably time to start taking part in pub quizzes now, what with the ever-growing list of trivia I've picked up along the way.

What I hadn't realised was the huge number of well-documented uses ginger has in the world of Asian medicine, or the way that ginger can ease travel sickness . . . or even headaches caused by dealing with information overload! Modern research is substantiating many claims from old established folk remedies. Unsurprisingly, these go back thousands of years, like a lot of other subjects I've researched.

Ginger has played a big part in the spice wars and medieval trade routes and was even thought to ward off plague during Tudor times. I still don't know how anyone ever thought of using it to keep horses' tails up during parades, but there we go: it just goes to show that ginger is hot stuff!

Where Does Ginger Come From?

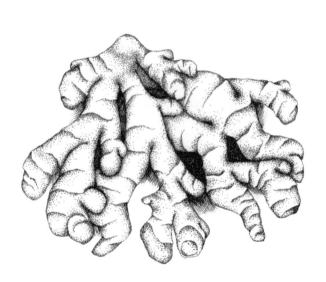

WHAT SORT OF A PLANT IS GINGER?

Ginger belongs to the family *Zingiberaceae*, a family that is comprised of around 45 genera and well over 1,000 species. This family of plants has many interesting relatives, including canna lilies, some banana species, turmeric and cardamom. If it is allowed to flower, beautiful lily- or orchid-like flowers will be produced, given the right conditions. Another plant in the family, galangal, is used for similar purposes to ginger in Thai cuisine.

Ginger as we know it is a rhizome or underground root of *Zingiber officinale*. We mostly refer to this as root ginger and it can be bought in various forms.

Today, ginger is naturalised in many parts of the world, although it probably originated in parts of Asia (India or China) thousands of years ago. Because it is relatively easy to grow and transplant, given the right conditions, it has been easily introduced to other continents.

Requirements for cultivation

Ginger needs rich, well-drained, moist soil and plenty of indirect sunlight and water. It is sensitive to frost, so is mostly confined to subtropical and tropical areas and climates. It grows best in fertile loams of tropical lowlands and forests which provide hot, shady and humid conditions and plenty of nutrients. Ginger has no growing season, so will grow throughout the year, under the right conditions. It needs a minimum annual rainfall of 150 cm (around 5 feet, or 60 inches) and temperatures of at least 30°C (86°F). In addition, a hot dry season is needed. A crop will start to shoot in ten days and takes about nine months to produce rhizomes for harvesting.

Characteristics

The rhizomes of *Zingiber officinale* grow as thick, beige, fleshy, finger-like branching underground stems. These rhizome stems produce a perennial reed-like plant growing from 1-1^1/$_2$ metres tall (3-4 feet).

White or yellowish-green flowers and ribbed leaves are borne on separate stems. Flower stems are shorter than leaf stems and the flowers appear at the apex of stems in dense cone-like spikes. These can be about 5-9 centimetres (2-3 inches) long. The leaves are bright green, smooth and tapering at both ends, just like those of the common forms of canna lily. From Asia ginger has spread to the West Indies, South America, western tropical Africa and Australia.

Growing as a pot plant and for interest

Zingiber officinale can be propagated from a healthy piece of root planted in spring. This is the most common way of increasing stock. I'm reliably informed that you can grow ginger that has been purchased from a supermarket in a pot on a windowsill, but I can't claim to have succeeded in this myself, yet, on my north-facing kitchen sill. However, the advice may prove an interesting challenge. I'm not sure that you'll get much of a ginger crop, or anything edible, either.

Choose ginger roots that already have some new buds appearing and have obviously not been treated to prevent more growth of the rhizomes. Plant the root so that it sticks out of the soil and water sparingly to prevent rot. Cover with a plastic bag and place it on a sunny windowsill. Remove the bag as soon as shoots appear. Provided it is left in a pot, in a warm spot with indirect sunlight and watered regularly, you may be rewarded with a green plant with glossy leaves. A greenhouse with some shade would seem to be the answer for growing the best plants, though achieving flowers might prove impossible from such rhizomes.

Ginger will not grow in temperatures lower than 28°C (82°F), but if you live in a climate warm enough to plant the ginger outside (i.e. not in the UK), plant in the ground for the summer but bring indoors before winter. This is the time to harvest any rhizomes. Dry the rhizomes to help preserve them. Store the remainder in a cool, dark place and ignore until spring. The plant might bounce back when growth continues the following spring, although you should expect to renew the rhizome, as damp winter conditions in the UK and low light levels are a bit of a problem for ginger.

OTHER TYPES OF GINGER AND RELATED SPECIES

Galangal

Galangal is also called Thai ginger. The word galangal is used as a common name for all members of the genus *Alpinia*. (This name, by the way, has nothing to do with mountain ranges or high meadows, but is the name of a 16th-century Italian botanist, Prospero Alpino.) Galangal is a plant very like common ginger, with an edible rhizome. It is native to Indonesia and China. St Hildegard of Bingen (1098—1179), an early herbalist, called galangal 'the spice of life' and wrote that it had been given by God to provide protection against illness. The name galangal is derived from the Arabic Khalanjan, and it has been suggested that it was perhaps originally from a Chinese word meaning 'mild ginger'.

Although it looks like ginger, lesser galangal (*Alpinia officinarum*) or greater galangal (*Alpinia galangal*) has a soapy, earthy smell and, although spicy, doesn't taste the same as *Zingiber officinale*. It can be bought as a powder or as whole rhizomes. Galangal and lime juice are mixed as a tonic in parts of South-East Asia. It is said to act as a stimulant and aphrodisiac.

Cardamom (*Elettaria* and *Amomum*)

There are two members of the ginger family that are known as cardamom. *Elettaria* and *Amomum* both produce small seed pods with a thin papery shell and small black seeds. *Elettaria* is the most common form and has green pods which are used as a flavouring, mainly for coffee and tea, where the spice is cooked along with coffee.

It is used as a spice, for chewing, smoking and in medicine. It is used to treat mouth and throat infections as well as digestive problems, the lungs and eye inflammation. It is also claimed to be an antidote for snake and scorpion venom.

Amomum pods are larger and dark brown. They are used in Indian medicine and traditional Chinese medicine for stomach upsets, constipation and dysentery. A lot of cardamom is grown in Nepal.

Fingerroot
In Thailand, several members of the *Zingiberaceae* family besides common ginger and turmeric are available in food markets. One of them, called fingerroot (*Boesenbergia pandurata*), has a characteristic appearance with several slender, long tubers sprouting in the same direction, just like a bunch of young, slender carrots.

Wild ginger
A native species of North America is known as 'wild ginger', and its root has some aromatic properties. It is not related to true ginger and should not be used as a substitute because it contains a carcinogen called aristolochic acid. It is not a member of the *Zingiberaceae* family, belonging instead to the *Aristolochiaceae* family. In fact, ginger does not grow naturally as a truly wild plant at all.

Myoga *Zingiber mioga* Roscoe
Zingiber mioga Roscoe is found in the woodlands of Japan and is now cultivated in Australia and New Zealand. In the USA it grows as an ornamental and is considered an invasive weed elsewhere. Young Myoga shoots are prized for their delicate ginger flavour and crisp texture. The new flower buds are sometimes

finely shredded and eaten in Japanese cuisine, but the older rhizomes and mature parts of the plant are toxic.

Turmeric (*Curcuma longa*)

Although not ginger, turmeric deserves a mention here as part of the *Zingiberaceae* family. Rhizomes are boiled for several hours and then dried in hot ovens before being ground into a deep-yellow powder. Turmeric is often used in recipes with ginger, especially in curries. Its active ingredient is curcumin. In Ayurvedic medicine, turmeric is thought to have many medicinal properties and many people in India use it as an antiseptic for cuts and burns. It is also used as an antibacterial agent. Turmeric is classified as E100 when used as a food additive and is used to protect food products from sunlight.

Zedoary (*Curcuma zedoaria*)

Zedoary is a perennial herb, with an underground stem or rhizome, very similar in appearance to ginger. The plant, native to India and Indonesia, was introduced to Europe by Arabs around the 6th century. The root smells faintly of mango although its flavour is more akin to ginger, except for a very bitter aftertaste. Zedoary is used in some traditional Eastern medicines where it is reputed to be good for the digestion, a relief for colic and purification for the blood. The essential oil produced from the dried roots is used in perfumery and soap-making, as well as in bitter tonics. Zedoary is rarely seen in other countries and has been largely replaced by ginger in popularity.

Exotic ginger plants

Whilst researching this book, I became aware of the dazzling array of species of ginger plants that grow in more hospitable climates than that in Britain. Ginger plants are often used as landscaping around subtropical houses. The flowers of many of these gingers are quite breathtakingly beautiful and truly exotic. They certainly provide food for thought: I feel a challenge in the offing for growing some as pot plants. I thought that the cannas, which grow everywhere around us in south-west France during the summer, were pretty spectacular, but now they seem quite tame. I've certainly looked at ginger in a different light!

Just look online for images of examples of some of the following varieties:

• Alpinia (bamboo ginger)
• Curcuma
• Kaempferia
• Globba
• Zingiber
• Etlingera
• Hedychium (butterfly ginger).

Generally, the Curcumas and Hedychiums are the most hardy, or so I'm told. I'm about to start growing some Hedychiums from seed, as I like a challenge. They are said to be the most fragrant.

Most gingers prefer bright, indirect light or filtered sunlight. To get gingers to flower you must provide them with enough light, so varieties that prefer shadier conditions tend to perform best indoors. Globbas (dancing ladies) and Kaempferias (peacock gingers) might be best. Alpinias have lovely foliage and like both light and filtered shade, so I'm giving them a go, too.

WAYS TO BUY GINGER

Ginger can be bought in various forms. Whenever possible, however, I like to use fresh ginger rather than the dried form of the spice. It not only has a superior flavour but contains higher levels of gingerol as well as anti-inflammatory properties. Fresh ginger root is sold in the produce section of markets and you sometimes have to look closely to find it. Make sure it is firm, smooth and not dried up.

NATURAL FORMS

Fresh ginger
Raw roots or rhizomes are generally referred to as fresh ginger. These provide the best flavour and have a pale yellow interior and skin which can vary in colour from brown to off-white. Jamaica ginger, which is beige, is regarded by many as the best variety, whereas African and Indian rhizomes are darker and generally of less good flavour. The exception to this is Kenyan ginger. Cochin has a very short rhizome and is coated in a red-grey colour. Fresh ginger root can be used for numerous dishes and can be prepared as a tea.

Some main varieties of ginger grown commercially:

TYPE	CHARACTERISTICS	COLOUR
Jamaica or White	Irregularly branched 4-16 cm (1.5-7 in) aromatic, pungent rhizomes free from outer corky layer.	Light brown-beige exterior with yellowy inside. Yellow oil cells.
African	Rhizomes with cork partly removed, wrinkled. Strong smelling and intensely pungent.	Darker brown to grey. Internally yellow or dark bluish; yellow oil cells and reddish resin cells.
Calcutta	Like African but with larger 'fingers'. Rather shrivelled in places. Good aroma and strong taste.	Grey-brown/grey-blue outside, light yellow inside; yellow oil and yellow-brown resin cells.
Calicut	Like African, aromatic with very strong flavour.	Uniformly light brown with light yellow interior; yellow oil and resin cells.
Cochin	Aromatic but not as strongly flavoured as African. Short rhizomes.	Light red/brown to grey with pale yellow inside; yellowy oil cells and red to black resin cells.
Japanese	Like Cochin but with thin coating of lime. Nearly smooth. Aromatic and pungent.	White/pale exterior with yellow, white or brown inside; brown/red resin cells.
Chinese	Coated rhizome, with short stumpy lobes. Mild flavour.	Pale exterior, lower in oil and resin.

Green ginger

Roots are collected and shipped when they are still immature, so the outer skin can be a light green colour. The rhizomes are not dried. This type can be found in oriental markets.

Dried ginger

Dried commercial gingers are sold with the root skin left on (black or coated) or with the skin peeled off (white or uncoated). It is really more beige than white.

Black roots are scalded in boiling water, then sun-dried. The white roots, considered the best, are scraped clean and dried, without being scalded. Dried ginger is usually found in rhizomes, but it can also be bought in slices. It is usually soaked in a recipe liquid before use.

Ground ginger

Although this has been processed by drying and making into a powder, I've included it here as opposed to the following section because it doesn't have anything else added to it. Ground ginger is quite different from the fresh rhizome and I have to admit that for many years I thought that the two were completely different varieties of the spice. Ground or powdered ginger is the buff-coloured ground spice made from dried root. It is readily available in supermarkets, and is used primarily in gingerbread, cakes and curry mixes, although I always use fresh ginger in curries and combine my own spices. You can't just substitute ground for fresh ginger in many recipes because they give different results.

PROCESSED FORMS OF GINGER

Ginger products are made from fresh or dried ginger root. They can also be distilled with steam from the oil in the root. Ginger is available today in extracts, tinctures, capsules and oils. Extracts of ginger are used in herbal remedies, foods, sweets, beverages, cosmetics and perfumes.

Preserved or stem ginger
For preserves fresh young green roots are used. First of all they are scalded and then rinsed in cold water before being peeled. The process is a lengthy one, with the water being changed several times. The process can take three or four days. The rhizomes are then put into jars and covered with a mild syrup. After a few days this is replaced by a stronger syrup which is, in time, again changed for a stronger one. Discarded syrups are sometimes fermented and made into a drink.

Sometimes a sugar–salt mixture is used to prepare preserved ginger. It is mostly used as a confection or to add to desserts. Try adding it to fresh pineapple: the combination is a delicious contrast of tropical fruit and hot spicy ginger.

Pickled ginger
Pickled ginger involves slicing the rhizome paper-thin and pickling it in a sweet vinegar and brine solution. This pickle is known in Japan as gari, and often accompanies sushi. It is often coloured red or pink and is served to refresh the palate between courses. It is also eaten as a breath freshener. I used some

recently for cooking with salmon. Although very salty because of the brine, it was delicious.

Crystallised ginger
Crystallised ginger is also cooked in sugar syrup, then air-dried and rolled in sugar. Production in China was said to be so small that there was only enough to supply the emperor Ming Tai Zu, who liked it very much. Crystallised ginger slices were called Ming ginger. Crystallised ginger is also known as candied ginger. It has been cooked in a sugar syrup until tender and then coated with granulated sugar.
It is used in desserts and can be made at home.

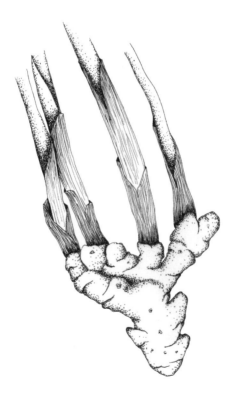

REGIONAL DIFFERENCES AND USES

Traditionally, Western cuisine has used ginger for sweet foods, such as gingerbread, biscuits, cakes and drinks. You'll find plenty of recipes for these in the recipe section. I think attitudes are changing, however, as tastes change and diets become more cosmopolitan. I was surprised to find my local supermarket shelf of root ginger completely empty the other Monday morning. When I asked if it had been moved, I was told that there had been a run on ginger over the previous day, because a TV chef had been using it over the weekend. On another visit I also observed an elderly lady breaking off small pieces of rhizome and popping them into a bag. What a shame, I thought: she could have bought a larger piece and have kept it for some time, instead of drying out the rest of the piece for some other, unsuspecting customer!

Alcoholic drinks

Jarnac, in France, is the home of a ginger-flavoured liqueur called Canton. This potent little brew is 28% alcohol (56 proof) and guaranteed to make your eyes water. The ingredients include syrup from caramelised ginger, cognac, champagne and orange blossom honey.

Green ginger wine used to be a favourite Christmas tipple, but nowadays the sugar content is too much for me. It's very warming, however, taken in small quantities, especially if you have a cold.

Ginger beer

Ginger beer was first brewed in the early 18th century and became very popular in Britain. There were apparently 3,000 breweries in Britain producing it in 1935. A non-alcoholic version is popular today as a fizzy drink (*see below*), although this uses yeast as a base and can, in some cases, become alcoholic and quite volatile. I once, in the early days of my teaching career, brewed it with the pupils as part of a lesson, in an army comprehensive school in Germany, where I worked in special needs. Apart from one bottle which blew up, the brew was enjoyed at the class Christmas party. It was only afterwards that word got around that I had been brewing on school premises and the lab where it fermented had a distinct smell of a brewery, much to the delight of some of my colleagues. The party was a great success as well, in that the pupils became sleepy towards the end, instead of winding themselves up as usual at the end of the day! You can find a recipe in a later section.

Soft drinks and beverages
In parts of the Middle East ginger is used to spice coffee. It is also used fresh to spice tea in India, especially in winter. In Indonesia people enjoy a beverage called *Wedang Jahe*, which is made from ginger and palm sugar. Find a recipe in a later section.

In the Ivory Coast, ground ginger is mixed with orange, pineapple and lemon to produce *Nyamanku*. Refreshingly spicy, I should imagine.

Ginger ale
Ginger ales come in two varieties: golden and dry. Golden ginger ale was developed first and dry ginger ale was developed during Prohibition in the USA. At this time ginger ale was used as a mixer for alcoholic drinks.

Ginger beer

Ginger beer can be a carbonated alcoholic beverage or a soft drink. It is flavoured with ginger, lemon and sugar. The recipe requires ginger, sugar and water which is added to a 'ginger beer plant'. I think my brother brought one home from Scouts once. We had ginger beer galore until we got fed up with it and had to 'let it go'. The 'plant' needed dividing every couple of weeks and rather than throw it away, the idea was to give it to a good home. Obviously everyone else felt the same. It was so much easier to buy fizzy drinks, anyway.

Ginger around the world

In India ginger comes in a variety of forms. There are oils and oleoresins as well as fresh ginger preserved in brine. Pickles are popular and ginger is a constituent of many. You can finde some recipes in the food section. Candied ginger and ginger in syrups are also sold. Ginger comes bleached or unbleached and in powder form. You wouldn't expect anything else from a country that produces so much ginger and uses spices heavily in cooking. Although ginger is grown all over India, the finest quality ginger is said to grow in Kerela. Dry ginger is known in the world market as Cochin ginger or Calicut ginger.

Fresh ginger is one of the main spices used for making pulse and lentil curries and is combined with other vegetable preparations. Ginger powder is, apparently, used in certain food preparations made especially for pregnant women and feeding mothers. The most popular is *Katlu*, a mixture of gum resin, ghee, nuts, ginger and sugar.

In southern India, ginger is used in the production of a sweet called *Inji-murappa* which is sold by street vendors. In Tamil Nadu, a less spicy variety of ginger is used when tender to make fresh pickle, combined with lemon juice or vinegar, salt and green chillies.

China's ginger is used for medicinal purposes as well as cooking. The juice from mature ginger roots is extremely potent and is often used to flavour seafood and lamb dishes. See the recipe section for ideas. It is also said to be perfectly suited for confectionery.

Ginger from Japan does not have a particularly good aroma. Pickled ginger (*gari*) is, as I said above, served as a condiment for sushi. Ginger products tend to vary considerably in different countries and the root varieties have differences due to the variety of the crop. For example, the Japanese use Myoga (see above) in sushi. It is said to have a delicate flavour of fresh water chestnut or very young sugar cane. The taste of ginger is faint, but easily recognised. In Burma ginger is used in a salad dish called gyin-tho: shredded ginger preserved in oil, nuts and seeds. The most unusual use I've come across is from the Philippines, where ginger is apparently used as bait to fish with. It is also chewed to drive out evil spirits which cause disease.

WHERE DOES GINGER GROW COMMERCIALLY TODAY?

From its beginnings in India and China ginger has become naturalised in many countries. It was transplanted to South America by Francisco de Mendosa in the 16th century. It is cultivated in the West Indies in vast quantities and is popular throughout the Caribbean. Nowadays, ginger is grown all over the tropics. The most expensive and highest quality varieties are said to come from Australia, southern India and Jamaica, while most mass-market ginger is grown in China. I haven't often been aware of where the ginger I buy comes from, but practically every country insists theirs is the best quality, it seems.

India produces a large amount of ginger for the domestic market. Likewise, different sources claim vastly differing quantities, so this section attempts to give the most up-to-date facts. Ginger does seem to be the most widely cultivated spice around the world and appears as different varieties. India is said to grow around 50 kinds and each sort will have a distinctive aroma and taste, depending on soil and growing conditions as well. African countries are said to grow pungent ginger, while milder varieties, which are made into powder, come from China. African and Cochin ginger yield the most resin and volatile oil.

In 2005 China appeared to lead the world in ginger production with a global share of almost 25%. Other major producers were India, Nepal and Indonesia. More recently ginger has been grown commercially in tropical parts of Australia and New Zealand.

Comparative figures for a number of countries date back some time.

Back in 2001 total world production of ginger stood at 835,000 tons. That's an awful lot of ginger! Most of the world trade in ginger is as a dried spice. India led the world in ginger production, with around 275,000 tons. This figure was closely followed by China and other leading producers.

World ginger production, 2001

COUNTRY	TONS
India	275,000
China	240,000
Nigeria	90,000
Indonesia	77,500
Bangladesh	42,000
Thailand	30,000
Philippines	29,000

Other countries that are growers and producers:

Australia	Fiji
Bhutan	Ghana
Brazil	Jamaica
Cameroon	Kenya
Costa Rica	Madagascar
Dominica	Malaysia
Dominican Republic	Mauritius
Ethiopia	Nepal

New Zealand
Pakistan
Republic of Korea
Réunion
Saint Lucia

Sierra Leone
Sri Lanka
Taiwan
Uganda

Confectionery ginger accounts for a tiny amount of trade (3%) by volume, but earns a much higher rate of return compared to fresh or dried ginger. Australia, China, Fiji and Thailand appear to be leaders in processing and exporting confectionery ginger.
Japan is the biggest importer of ginger by far, with over 100,000 metric tons in 2000. The USA came second with 19,000 metric tons and, surprisingly for a small country, the UK annually imports about 10,000 metric tons. These imports come from, in descending order of quantities, Thailand, Brazil, China, Nigeria and India, along with some other minor producers. Maybe it's our Indian empire connection that makes the UK such a big importer.

Ginger oil and oleoresin are produced mainly by India and China and find their way mainly to the USA, Europe and Japan. Find out more about oils and resins in the next section.

Globally, ginger represents about 15% of the tonnage of spices imported. In the USA, ginger has risen to be amongst the top 12 spices consumed, replacing fennel seeds.

The History Behind Ginger

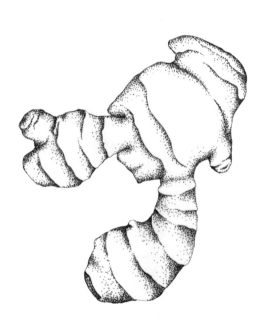

A BRIEF HISTORY OF THE USES OF GINGER

'Let thy food be thy medicine and thy medicine be thy food.'
HIPPOCRATES (460–377 BC)

This chapter aims to give a whistle-stop tour through thousands of years and cultural traditions and, as such, it is undoubtedly flawed in places, given the range of ideas and cultures involved. I've endeavoured to cover the subject chronologically, without getting too bogged down in philosophical debate or dwelling too long on ancient history and Indian or Chinese culture.

Spicing up early times

If you think that ginger is just a brown spicy powder to add to cakes, think again! The uses of ginger for medicinal and culinary applications go back thousands of years. Ginger was, during the days of spice trading before Christ, a major player in the trade of exotic and sought-after commodities. The first uses appear to have come from India and China a long time before then: at least 3,000 years ago and probably much earlier than that.

The name ginger comes from the Greek *zingiberis*. This word comes from Sanskrit, where it was known as *singabera* or *shringavera*. Archaeological evidence suggests that Bronze Age tablets found in Ancient Greek sites in Crete, Mycenae and Pylos date from approximately 1300–1400 BC. These tablets show plants, herbs and aromatic spices including ginger, that were used during the early Greek period.

GINGER IN CHINA

Ginger (*chiang*) was mentioned by the philosopher Confucius (551–479 BC) in his Analects.

In 1027 BC the Zhou Dynasty began and lasted until 221 BC. Chinese rule was extended during this period and trade with other nations increased. During this era there were no less than four kinds of royal doctors. One type was in charge of the emperor's health care and health preservation, and was responsible for preparing diets for him.

The Zhou Dynasty was replaced by the Han Dynasty and by around 200 BC Chinese culture had produced excellent craftsmanship, prized for its beauty. When the Han emperors extended territorial control over Central Asia during their 400-year reign, merchants travelled to Rome in safety, with cumin, ginger and cinnamon as well as silk and precious stones like jade. This overland trek from China followed various routes, depending on political stability and taxes in the intervening lands.

In the book said to have been written by Zhang Zhongjing, a noted medical man in the East Han Dynasty in about AD 200, some important medicated diet recipes were recorded, including one called 'Soup of Chinese angelica root, fresh ginger and mutton'.

Shennong's Herbal Classic, said to have been produced round about the Han period, is the earliest book surviving on plant medicines. Many sorts of medicaments, both herbs and food, were recorded, such as Chinese date, sesame seed, Chinese yam, grape, walnut kernel, lily bulb and fresh ginger.

One in 2,000

During the 16th century, Li Shizhen's *Compendium of Materia Medica* was published, chronicling centuries of Chinese medical achievement. It is packed with information on traditional Chinese medicine and prescribed treatments. It discusses almost 2,000 herbs and contains a separate section on 20 essential oils. It noted that ginger could be used to treat coughs and malaria. This book improved the biological classification of both plants and animals, in much the same way as the Greek Dioscorides' work of the same name had done, centuries earlier.

Ancient Chinese remedies mention both the fresh and dried roots of ginger. The fresh root was used to induce sweating, and the dried root for relieving pains in the stomach and abdomen. Ginger was popular in Chinese culture and fishermen are said to have known for centuries that ginger can stave off seasickness.

Taoism originated in China 2,000 years ago. It is a philosophy, a religion and also the basis for traditional Chinese medicine, encompassing over 5,000 years of wisdom and history. Together with Confucianism and Buddhism, it has been a guiding force in China. Everything, including the universe, is changing all the time. Relative stability can be achieved when a harmony is reached between *Yin* and *Yang*, which are said to be the opposite but related natural forces in the universe. There are five elements in everything: earth, metal, water, wood and fire. In the Chinese medical tradition plants and other ingredients are classified by five tastes, namely sweet, sour, bitter, pungent and salty. These corresponded with the five elements.

Chinese medicine is also based on the balance between *Yin* and *Yang* in the organs. A blockage in the channels of life forces to the lungs leads to tissues becoming stagnant. This leads to a build-up of toxins, creating disease. Ginger is classified as a warming herb, which affects the channels of the spleen, stomach and lungs. The lungs and large intestine form the metal part of the elements and the health of the lungs depends on the health of the intestines. Intestines in poor health can, therefore, cause conditions such as asthma. Ginger is indicated for the treatment of nausea, headaches and poor digestion, as well as colds and coughs. Other foods considered healing to the metal element include brown rice, green vegetables, fish, garlic and pears.

At the same time, the use of aromatics also progressed. Taoists believed that extraction of a plant's fragrance liberated its soul. Like the Greeks, the Chinese used one word, *heang*, to represent perfume, incense and fragrance. Six aesthetic moods were identified, broadly described as tranquil, reclusive, luxurious, beautiful, refined or noble.

Tang to Ming
Between the 7th and 17th centuries the Chinese upper classes were mad on fragrance, using scented wood to make statues and fans. Sachets of fragrance would be thrown at audiences during dance performances. Along with jasmine oils from India, Persian rose water, Indonesian cloves, ginger, nutmeg and patchouli were used extensively. Bodies, clothes, homes and temples were perfumed as well as paper, ink, baths and cosmetics. Perfumed sachets were frequently concealed in clothing.

Herbal teas

Herbal teas were an important part of traditional Chinese medicine. Some of these are still enormously popular today (*see the health section*). The addition of ginger made a naturally warming infusion.

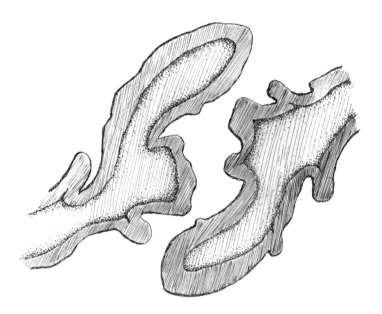

GINGER IN THE INDIAN SUBCONTINENT

Ayurvedic medicine
Ginger has been used in India from extremely ancient times. Indian medicine probably developed in the Indus Valley civilisation, dating from 3000 BC. Ayurvedic medicine is a holistic system which focuses on the connection between all aspects of a healthy body and a healthy mind. An imbalance of forces can be corrected using certain spices. For thousands of years ginger, along with other herbs and spices, has been used to treat such ailments as arthritis.

It was between 1200 BC and 700 BC that sacred writings (Vedas) were composed. These refer in some detail to medical and scientific matters relating to diseases, herbs and herbal cures. By the time of Buddha, around 520 BC, Ayurvedic practice was flourishing and it continued to do so until the arrival of the British.

The central concept of Ayurvedic medicine is the theory of a balance between three bodily humours (dosas). When these humours, wind (Vata), bile (Pitta) and phlegm (Kapha) are in equilibrium, the body enjoys perfect health. Any imbalance will cause ill health. Ayurveda teaches that the humours need to be kept in check through practising a healthy, moderate lifestyle regarding sleep and diet. Treatments include forms of purification through sweating, vomiting and enemas, to remove excessive humours. Ayurvedic remedies are said to act by protecting the body from excess humours and by counteracting the excessive humour. There are six tastes identified: sour, sweet, bitter, pungent, salty and astringent. These correspond with the five elements of earth, air, fire, water and space, varying slightly from the Chinese tradition mentioned above.

Susruta II, a physician in the 2nd century AD, made frequent references to uses of herbs and spices covering the period back to about 500 BC. Susruta II listed over 700 drugs of plant origin, including cinnamon, cardamom, ginger, turmeric, and various kinds of pepper. Turmeric, which is related to ginger, has held a place as one of the most important healing spices since ancient times.

Unani medicine
This type of medicine is closely related to Ayurvedic medicine. Originating in ancient Greece, the principles of Unani medicine date back to Hippocrates (*see below*). Unani medicine came to the Indian subcontinent around AD 1100 and is closely linked with Muslim beliefs.

Indian cuisine
In India wealthy people feasted on refined and expensive foods at festivals and religious celebrations. The preference for particular foods denoted caste, religious beliefs and ethnic group. Ginger is used extensively today in curry pastes for dishes from northern India, as well as in Gujarati cooking from western India. You can find some simple, anglicised recipes for spicy Indian dishes in the recipe section.

The *Mahabharata*, a Hindu epic written in the 4th century BC, shows that ginger was being used in those times for cooking with meat and other spices. The *Manasollasa* was written during the 11th century and encapsulates 'That which exhilarates the mind'. It also contains a reference to ginger being used to flavour buttermilk. During Muslim rule between the 10th and 12th centuries, there was a great mixing of cuisines and traditions within Indian, Persian and Middle Eastern cooking. The *Ni'matnamah*, or Book of Delights, which survives from the end of the 14th century, lists recipes and remedies from central India. Unsurprisingly, it details the wide variety of ingredients to be used, including ginger.

The Hindu influences on Indian cooking from the 14th to the 16th centuries are still evident today in the dishes of Southern India. Mangoes, limes and ginger were amongst the inexpensive ingredients available to all in the markets. Meals often began with pickles of ginger, mango and lemon. This tradition later continued under mogul influence.

Under mogul rule during the 16th and 17th centuries, Indian cuisine took on even more Persian elements. The moguls were descended from Genghis Khan, so lavish dishes and communal eating reached the height of sophistication. One recipe from this time apparently was for making a pudding from garlic and ginger for special occasions.

OTHER ANCIENT PEOPLE

Babylonians and Ancient Egyptians may have used ginger in cooking, although there are few references and little tangible proof. The Ancient Egyptians, however, believed ginger to be an aphrodisiac, along with fennel, pomegranates, coriander and radishes with honey. Ancient Mediterranean and Middle Eastern cuisines used dried ginger, as this form could be transported unspoiled after the voyage from East Asia and India. As Greek and Roman civilisations declined, Greek medical texts survived in the Islamic courts of medieval times. In the 8th and 9th centuries many of the original texts were translated into Arabic or Persian.

The ancient silk and spice routes

In the 4th century BC Alexander the Great inherited vast information about spices and the spice trade in the ancient Near East and northern India. Scientific knowledge and botanical studies of spices and herbs also flourished. With the conquering of Egypt in 332 BC, Alexander the Great created major trading centre at Alexandria for spices coming from the Orient to Europe. Here on the Mediterranean coast of Egypt, African and Asian spice traders conducted their trade with their Western counterparts. Persian traders carried, amongst other things, ginger and cinnamon, roses, orris root, saffron, nutmeg, black pepper and the gum resins frankincense and myrrh.

Caravans came from India, China and South-East Asia. These were taken by ship across the Greek and Roman Mediterranean. The vast demand for spices was also served by overland caravans from Sinai, Petra and Jerusalem — more familiar today as Jordan, Israel and

Syria — into Turkey and Europe. Evidence of this has been uncovered by archaeologists across the eastern Mediterranean.

Around 285 BC to 250 BC a canal connecting the Nile with the Red Sea provided further benefit to trade. Demand continued to increase, as cooking began to rely heavily on spices which were now well known. The Greeks used a wide variety of spices for cooking as well as for medicinal treatments: salt was essential for curing meats and was used frequently as a preservative; spices like ginger and pepper helped to improve the flavour of some of the rather unpalatable dishes.

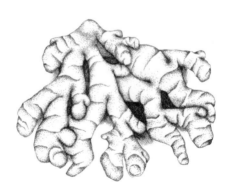

EARLY GREEK AND ROMAN
USES OF GINGER

Even before the time of Hippocrates, other leading Greek philosophers and scientists were extolling the virtues of ginger. Pythagoras was a great believer in the healing power of ginger. By around the 4th century BC Hippocrates, the father of modern medicine, was using ginger with a variety of other spices in medicines in Greece. Peppers and spices were used in wine as medications for stomach pain. Hippocrates based his medicine on an understanding of four humours, defined as blood, phlegm, black bile and yellow bile. Each humour was cold or hot and wet or dry. Interestingly, this belief was much travelled and still formed the basis of diagnosis in Tudor Britain (*see Culpeper below*). It isn't clear where these ideas originated, although the Greeks were heavily influenced by the Egyptians and imported many of their substances and ideas into their own medical repertoire.

A hundred years later, around 300 BC, Theophrastus suggested that spices like ginger could aid digestion. Theophrastus is regarded as the founder of botany, and his book entitled *Historia Plantarum* (A History of Plants, or A Treatise on Plants) became the basis for plant classification for centuries afterwards.
He explained where plants were found, what their uses were and also their basic elements. He also tried to define the mechanics of smell. Aristotle, a predecessor of Theophrastus, had tried to account for the five senses but found the sense of smell harder to define than the others, concluding that humans had a poor sense of smell compared with animals.

A drop of poison, anyone?

Poisoning was popular amongst the ancient peoples of Greece and Rome. King Mithridates VI of Pontus (132–63 BC) apparently liked to find antidotes by experimenting with poisons on his prisoners.

His experiments led him to declare that he had discovered an antidote for snake bites and poisonous substances. He mixed all the effective antidotes into a single one, called *mithridatium* or *mithridate*. This contained opium, myrrh, saffron, ginger, cinnamon and castor, along with about 40 other ingredients. The Roman Emperor Nero's physician Andromachus improved upon the antidote by increasing the list of ingredients to 64, including viper's flesh. There are no records of recovery rates, but this antidote became known as *Theriaca andromachi* and later as Venice Treacle. Galen later wrote about antidotes, and credited the King of Pontus with creating a *mithridatium* containing 41 ingredients.

Dioscorides, a Greek physician who travelled widely, wrote *De Materia Medica* in about 70 BC. A work of many volumes, it was to become the most important handbook for plant drugs for centuries to come and was widely used all over Europe until the Middle Ages. Dioscorides was a physician to the Roman armies, so he had plenty of opportunity to travel and observe new species of plants, learning about their properties along the way. He combined this knowledge of botany with medicinal and therapeutic uses.

Concerning odours

Most of Theophrastus' works concentrated on the medicinal qualities and unusual features of plants, but he also included a section entitled *De Odoribus*, or 'Concerning Odours', which underscored his belief that every substance had a certain odour which was related to its function. Much later, works by Locke, a 17th-century philosopher in England, supported these views.

It seems that most of us today still have little more idea than the ancient Greek philosophers about how smells are experienced or of their make-up, although the modern world is still obsessed with perfumes, fragrances and smells to cover up other smells and 'improve' the environment. Theophrastus' ideas on smell were substantiated in part by the work of 18th-century French chemists Fourcry, Lavoisier and Berthollet, concerning gases and a chemical system of naming compounds. There's little wonder, then, that the spice trade of pre-Christian times included strongly aromatic plants and resins, which were so important in terms of ritual, as well as covering up the unpleasant odours of early civilisations, when people had not discovered methods for preserving and deodorising. At one point, ginger was considered almost as important as pepper in the spice trade.

THE ROMAN INFLUENCE

After Rome took over Egypt in 30 BC, there was an even greater flood of spices into the Mediterranean from India via the Red Sea canal and then on to Greece and Italy. The Romans had different ideas about spices, however, and these were no longer confined to medicinal or ceremonial use, as they had been by the Eygptians. Basically, any application was up for grabs, although the Romans did learn of medical uses as well.

The Romans were perhaps the most lavish users of aromatic spices. They incorporated them into cosmetics and used them to throw along the path during rites such as funeral processions. Even soldiers used perfumes from the East.

Plagues were common and aromatic resins were burned to keep away bad spirits and demons. As a note of interest, this is where the word 'perfume' comes from: *Per*, meaning through, and *fumus* the Latin for 'smoke'. Trying to placate the gods in charge of diseases seems a little tame nowadays. Roman perfumes followed Greek traditions but one of the popular scents appears to have been made by mixing sandalwood or musk with cinnamon, ginger and vanilla.

Spice-flavoured wines were popular, as were balms and oils for use after visiting the baths. The addition of spices thickened the oils as well as making them more fragrant. Lamp oil was also treated with pungent fragrance to keep harmful vapours at bay. Many Romans believed that sleeping on saffron-filled pillows would ward off a hangover the next day. Spices such as ginger were used in poultices and healing preparations.

Pliny the Elder
Luckily, other more scientific minds were focused on plant use for medicines. Pliny the Elder, a naturalist until his untimely death at Pompeii in AD 79, recorded that the ancient Romans ate the shoots of the ginger plant. He also had some firm views on the spice trade and the inflated prices caused, apparently, by women wanting the latest new imports of silks and other exotic items. He also mentioned a plant from India, similar in appearance to ginger, but tasting like saffron.

Apicius

This is the name given to a collection of recipes that was probably compiled in the4th or early 5th centuries AD. A gourmet called Marcus Gavius Apicius, who lived in the first century AD, is sometimes credited with the recipes, but *Apicius* was actually compiled around 300 years later. The Roman gourmet cook had a large choice of aromatic herbs and spices centred mainly on pepper, saffron, cardamom and a type of giant fennel. Ginger was rarely cited and cinnamon was used as a medicine. The books became popular much later in about 1500, when early editions were printed in Milan and Venice.

Included in *Apicius* is a 'Summary of spices which should be in the house so that nothing is lacking in seasoning'. There doesn't seem much chance of that happening, however, given the list:

saffron
pepper
ginger
laser or asafoetida
folium
myrtle berries
costmary
cloves
addenda
cardamom
spikenard or Indian spike (another aromatic rhizome)

A potted salad includes instructions to mix celery seed, mint, pennyroyal (a type of mint), ginger, coriander, raisins and honey with vinegar, olive oil and wine. This was to be mixed and then poured over chicken, goat sweetbreads and bread with cheese, pine nuts, cucumber and dried onion. That doesn't sound too bad, apart from the goat bits or 'glandules'. Chicken and ginger go very well together (*see the recipe section*).

Another recipe for a sauce for roasted meat (*Aliter Assaturas*) from late Roman times gives a complicated mix of spices:

> *6 scruples each of parsley, hazelwort, ginger,*
> *5 laurel berries, sufficient seasoning, 6 scruples*
> *each of asafoetida root, origan, and cyperus,*
> *a little costmary, 3 scruples of pyrethrum,*
> *6 scruples of celery-seed, 12 scruples of pepper*
> *and sufficient liquamen and oil.*

Costmary was a popular medieval herb like tansy, smelling of balsamica. Cyperus, out of interest, was used by the Chinese for strong and pleasant fragrances, such as those occurring in culinary spices, perfumes and incense. It is known as nutsedge and is a notorious weed. Liquamen was a very potent sauce made from fish left to ferment in salt. All in all, I think we can be sure that the ginger wouldn't have been an overpowering flavour, given the list of ingredients!

Anthimus

Anthimus was a Greek from Byzantium who served the king of Reims in north-east France in the sixth century. He listed healthy and unhealthy foods in a book and advised against excess, although the barbarous lords he served were probably none the wiser. Anthimus followed the theories of Hippocrates and the four humours, and he advocated the use of ginger for many ailments because of its heat and moisture-giving qualities. His recipes contain a lot more ginger than those in the *Apicius*.

Roman tax

The Romans seemed to have sussed out the spice trade quite well, under the theory of 'If it's popular, tax it'. Little detail seems now available, apart from the fact that, in the 2nd century AD, ginger was a good source of tax revenue, along with other spices.

Ginger dries up

In the 4th century AD, the Emperor Constantine founded Constantinople on the site of the Greek city of Byzantium, known today as Istanbul. It became the greatest centre in the Near East for trade in spices prized by the Romans. But, as the Roman Empire faltered and came to an end in the 5th century, Arabs took over the spice trade. Pots of ginger rhizomes were carried on long sea voyages from China to South-East Asia and the plant spread to other countries along the way. However, ginger and many other spices became expensive again and their use dwindled, almost to the point of drying up completely.

MEDIEVAL GINGER

Use of ginger developed slowly during the Middle Ages. It was said to have been found in one quarter of all medieval French and English recipes, although it was used less in Italy and Spain. At least three different kinds of ginger were used then, reportedly called common ginger, white ginger from India and ginger that had passed in transit through the holy city of Mecca and was probably thought to have extra properties. Following remedies of the Arabs, European herbalists of the Middle Ages produced drinks and other preparations by mixing sweet syrups of violets and roses with spices such as ginger, pepper, nutmeg, cinnamon, saffron, cardamom and herbs.

European trading
The Dark Ages, from 600 to 1100, yield little information as to the use of oriental spices in northern Europe, although trade was greatly reduced once the trade routes were blocked by various groups and warring factions. By the end of the 10th century, the spice trade dealt mainly with pepper, cinnamon, ginger and galangal (*see the previous chapter*). Other spices were not common across Europe for everyday use in cooking until the 13th or 14th centuries. Variations occurred across Europe because of price, availability and even trends and social status. Small amounts were also procured by the Church.

The spice of life
The Crusades kick-started economic activity as well as religious wars. Competition between Mediterranean ports for trade resulted in Venice and Genoa in Italy benefiting greatly from these expeditions; the great wealth of Venice at the time is said to have originated from the spice trade. Venice dominated

the trade in spices and had a virtual monopoly on some of them. Spices were transported to the north on overland routes by packhorse up the Rhône Valley and later, after the early 13th century, by galley to the ports of Holland, Germany, France, Belgium and England.

From Venice, ship owners were given landing rights to establish trading centres across the Holy Land. The sheer numbers of soldiers involved in the Crusades must have generated huge trading opportunities in wool, metal, food and clothing. These were exchanged for fruit, precious stones and spices, which were all imported through Italy.

The influence of the Hanseatic League, which began in the 13th century, established trade across the Baltic and North Sea in English cloth, sea salt, corn, iron and oriental spices. This alliance lasted until the 17th century. Some trade was conducted along the rivers of Russia to the Baltic. Trade was carried across the sea to London, including cargoes of pepper, cinnamon and ginger, which were exchanged for wool. Spices were so precious that it is said that a pound of ginger could fetch the price of a whole sheep.

Tastes to avoid like the plague

Considering the often unpleasant and limited food supplies available to the average medieval European, it is not difficult to understand why any additional flavouring was welcome. Spices like ginger, pepper, cardamom and cinnamon could do wonders to a lump of carcass that might have been lying around, preserved in salt, for months during the winter. Aromatic spices also covered up unpleasant odours and were important when other herbs and vegetables were out of season. Spiced wines were also very popular until tea, coffee, cocoa and sugar were available in later years.

But poor-tasting food was the least of the problems that many of the populations of the time had to worry about. The Crusades had brought Europe closer to Asia, but also brought outbreaks of plague. Between AD 1339 and 1351, the pandemic of plague travelled from China to Europe, carried by rats and fleas along the silk caravan routes and sea routes. In 1347 the Black Death appeared in Italy, arriving on spice ships via Asia and North Africa, courtesy of the fleas on rats aboard the ships. Between 1347 and 1350, an estimated 75 million people are thought to have died of the plague. Twenty-five million of these lived in Europe, with few countries or even fewer communities escaping the disease, which inconveniently travelled along the now established trade routes across Europe. More than a quarter of the entire population is thought to have been wiped out.

Aside from plague and poor food, influential, rich hosts during the feudal Middle Ages liked to impress or maybe even intimidate their guests with the liberal use of spices. Expensive imports could be added in complex mixtures to each course and were also added to wines, to reflect the wealth, power and initiative of the host.

Polo discovers spice mint
Another 13th-century development in spices, with a much better outcome for all concerned, came as a result of the travels of Marco Polo. A curtain of exclusion — which had lasted for about 600 years between Asia and Europe — was lifted and the flow of ideas and goods was revitalised. During 1298 or

thereabouts, Marco Polo was imprisoned in Genoa for a year, during a war between Venice and Genoa, who obviously argued a lot about trade. He dictated memoirs of his travels to another prisoner, frequently describing spices, including the huge volume of trade in pepper, the flavour of sesame oil in Afghanistan and the vast plantings of ginger and cassia, a cinnamon like plant, growing around Kain-du, previously called Peking and now known as Beijing. This was the capital of Kublai Khan, where people drank rice wine highly flavoured with spices.

Marco Polo not only described coastal regions, like some, later explorers, but showed a lot of insight into the inland continent of Asia. He reported that rich people ate meat pickled in salt and flavoured with spices, while the poor had to make do with garlic. Polo described in detail vast plantings of pepper, nutmeg, cloves and other spices he had seen growing in Java and throughout the islands of the China Sea. He also recalled the abundance of ginger, cinnamon and pepper on the coasts of India and East Africa:

> There is great abundance of pepper and also of ginger, besides cinnamon in plenty and other spices, turbit and coconuts. Buckrams are made here of the loveliest and most delicate texture in the world. In return, when merchants come here from overseas, they load their ships with brass, which they use as ballast, cloth of gold and silk, sandal, gold, silver, cloves, spikenard and other such spices that are not produced here... Goods are exported to many parts.

The port of Aden, 'The port to which all the ships from India come', was described, along with the method by which goods made their way on small boats along the Red Sea, a journey of seven days. The goods were then transferred to camels for a month-long trek overland to the Nile, Alexandria and then Europe.

Not everyone believed these stories, but gradually merchants and explorers from Europe realised that these regions could be reached by ship. Unknowingly, Marco Polo had started an 'Age of Exploration'.

GINGER IN BRITAIN

Ginger was probably first brought to England by the Romans, but the spice does not appear to have been well known or well used at that time. By the Norman Conquest, however, it was often referred to in Anglo-Saxon leech-books.

A nation of grocers?

In 12th-century England a guild was established for the sale of pepper. This Guild of Pepperers was based in Blackfriars in London and later became a more general spice guild, later still, during the 15th century, becoming a grocers' company. The guild was given a charter by King Henry VI to sell wholesale goods. This is where, by the way, we get the word 'grocer' from: the French for wholesale is *en gros*. They were licensed to trade in precious spices, medicines and dye stuffs. As another note of interest, the French word for spice is *épice* and a grocery shop is called an *épicerie* (in French, an 'é' denotes a missing 's'). Grocers had exclusive rights to 'garble', i.e. clean, separate and select spices. There's another word with an interesting history: 'garble' comes from an Arabic word, *gharbala*, meaning to sift and select. It might be interesting to discover at which point the more modern meaning of talking nonsense/being selective with the truth took over.

The grocers often came from Italy and were connected with Italian merchants who had settled in London. They became responsible for garbling spices and also for regulating the weighing of all heavy imported goods, using the King's Beam. Used for several hundred years, this was a standard balance for weighing wholesale goods.

At this time medicine still adhered to the views of Hippocrates and the four humours (blood, phlegm, yellow bile and black bile). Dioscorides' work, *De Materia Medica*, was still the textbook of plants, herbs and spices until at least the 17th century, so you can see why spices were so important in many countries. Spices were thought to improve health and influence corresponding moods: sanguine, phlegmatic, choleric and melancholic. Ginger was thought to heat the stomach and improve digestion.

Some of the original spicers later became powerful apothecaries, taking the drug business from the grocers, and later on becoming physicians. A further point of (linguistic) interest, if you are still awake, is that pepper, one of the most highly sought-after and prized spices, was sometimes sold by the peppercorn, because of the high price. It was also used as currency and paid out in dowries and spoils of war. Spices cost almost twice as much in England as they did in the South of France during the Middle Ages. What price a 'peppercorn rent'?

Fourteenth century bread hard to swallow?
Gingerbread is said to have originated in Ancient Greece, as a means to avoid indigestion after overeating. A piece of ginger wrapped in bread eventually became gingerbread. Whether this is true or not, a type of gingerbread was popular, although not resembling many of today's recipes. At one time the word 'gingerbread' was used to describe preserved ginger. This was typical of the many sweets brought to Chaucer's Sir Thopas in *The Canterbury Tales*:

A roial spicerye of gyngebreed that was ful fyn

By the 15th century it had become a dense dough made from breadcrumbs and ground almonds mixed with honey or spices. Often this dough was pressed into fancy moulds. There were many varieties of gingerbread in medieval times, including coarse, fine and red, which was coloured with sandalwood and wine. Gilded gingerbread contained real gold. You'll find some recipes that are a little easier to follow in the recipe section!

This recipe dates from the 15th century:

> *Gyngerbrede*
> *Take a quart of honey and sethe it and skime it clene; take Safroun, pouder Pepir and throw theron; take gratyd Brede and make it so chargeant that it wol be y-lechyd; then take pouder canelle and straw ther-on y-now; then make it square, lyke as thou wolt leche yt; take when tho lechyst hyt, an caste Box leves a-bowyn, y-stykyd ther-on, on clowys.*

The last part of this recipe suggests decorating the gingerbread with box leaves, fastened to each piece with a clove, in case you were struggling.

Other unusual recipes with ginger include the following:
• Venison pie with ginger
• Roast heron with ginger sauce
• Peacock with ginger
• Cheese and chicken meatballs with ginger

Tudor England
Henry VIII (1491–1547) is recorded as having instructed ginger to be used as a means of sweating out fever and avoiding the plague. There is no proof

that ginger would have any positive effect against plague, but I suppose trying anything was better than nothing. There are various recipes of the time that include ginger in their list of ingredients.

Medicine at this time was still based on the four humours. For example, blood was hot and wet, phlegm wet and cold. The humours were produced during digestion. Ill health arose from disharmony of the humours and medicines could re-establish their balance of the humours. For example, a 'hot' medicine would treat a 'cold' disease.

Recipes in 16th- and 17th-century England
Ginger had become a regular addition to recipes by this time, if the works of Gerard, Culpeper and May are anything to go by. In 1597, John Gerard, a noted physician and herbalist of the day, wrote the following entry in *Herball* for ginger:

> *Ginger, as Dioscorides reporteth, is right good with meate in sauces, or otherwise in conditures: for it is of an heating and digesting qualitie canded, greene or condited it gently looseth the belly, and is profitable for the stomach, and effectually opposeth itself against all darkness of the light; answering the qualities and effects of pepper. It is to be considered that candied green or condited ginger is hot and moist in qualitie, provioking Venerie: and being dried, it heateth or drieth in the third degree.*

By 'provioking Venerie' Gerard meant that ginger could be considered an aphrodisiac, obviously heating more than the stomach.

By the time of Elizabeth I gingerbread was slightly more refined, but still being made with stale bread, such as the manchets described here:

> *To make red Ginger-bread, commonly called Leach-lumbar.*
> *Grate and dry two stale Manchets, either by the fire, or in an Ouen, sift them through a Sieve, and put to it Cinamon, Ginger, Sugar, Liquorice, Anis-seed: when you haue mingled all this together, boile a pint of red wine, and stirre it, that it be as thick as a Hastie-pudding; then take it out, and coole it, and mould it with Cinamon, Ginger, Liquorice, and Anise-seede, and rowle it thinne, and print it with your mould, and dry it in a warme Ouen.*

White gingerbread was really more like marzipan:

> *To make white Ginger-bread*
> *Take halfe a pound of March-pane-Past made with Almonds, Rose-water and Sugar, and a spoonefull of Aqua-vita, season it very hot with Ginger, mould it up stiffe, rowle it thin, and print it with your moulds.*

Marzipan, or marchpane (March bread), is generally considered to be of Arabic origin. By the late 1600s, marzipan recipes come in many variations. Several books suggest adding other spices such as cinnamon or ginger if they have been finely sieved. The recipe makes the paste and then shapes the items that are desired in just the same way as gingerbread. One book from 1584 even describes how to use gold leaf to cover a tart.

Culpeper the chemist

Nicholas Culpeper was an apothecary in 17th-century London. His *Complete Herbal* listed the following comments about ginger and galangal. Notice the references to the Greek medicines of the humours and the classification of herbs.

> *Galangæ, majoris, minoris.*
> *Galanga, commonly called Galingal, the greater and lesser. They are hot and dry in the third degree, and the lesser are accounted the hotter, it strengthens the stomach exceedingly, and takes away the pains thereof coming of cold or wind; the smell of it strengthens the brain, it relieves faint hearts, takes away windiness of the womb, heats the reins, and provokes amorous diseases. You may take half a dram at a time.*

> *Hot in the third degree*
> *Angelica, Aron, Birthwort long and round, Sowbread, Asarabacca, Briony, white and black, Sallendine, Virginian snakeroot, Hemeric, White Dittany, Doronicum, Hellebore, white and black, Elicampane, Fillipendula, Galanga greater and lesser, Masterwort, Orris English and Florentine, Restharrow, stinking Gladen, Turbith, Ginger.*

For the bowels Culpeper suggested taking 'Valerian great and small, Zedoary, Ginger'. Ginger was also advocated for the joints.

Robert May

This recipe, for preparing a calf's tongue, comes from Robert May's *The Accomplisht Cook* (1660). He used ginger as a stuffing. I don't think I'll try it though.

Take a fresh Neats tongue raw, make a hole in the lower end and take out some of the meat, mince it with some bacon or beef-suet, and some sweet herbs, and put in the yolks of an egg or two, some nutmeg, salt, and some grated parmisan or fat cheese, pepper and ginger; mingle all together, and fill the hole in the tongue, then wrap a caul or skin of mutton about it, and binde it about the end of the tongue, boil it till it will blanch.

You get the picture, anyway. The recipe describes several other stages, involving claret, strong broth, cloves, mace, salt, pepper, bread, herbs chopped small, marrow, fried onions and apples.

Ipocras
Another favourite of the time was Ipocras or Hippocras, a spiced wine that was popular in medieval Europe and named after tonics that were prescribed by Hippocrates: a typical recipe would include pepper, cinnamon, ginger, melegueta (an African Guinea pepper), nutmeg, galingale and honey in wine. Other sweetened, spiced wines were used for pleasure or to treat various diseases. The warming qualities derived from peppercorns would make these wines suitable for use on cold evenings or for diseases characterised by an excess of cold humours. Examples would be the excessive phlegm of respiratory conditions. They are not a million miles from the spiced wines, ciders and mead consumed today at Christmas time.

This recipe dates from the 17th century, but it's not on my list of Christmas drinks!

Take a gallon of wine, three ounces of cinamon, two ounces of ginger, a quarter of an ounce of cloves, an ounce of mace, twenty corns of pepper, an ounce of nutmegs, three pounds of sugar, and two quarts of cream.

Mithridate

Nicholas Culpeper declared that garlic was full of virtues and was cheap enough to make it the 'poor-man's treacle'. The properties of garlic are well known, but the reference to treacle comes from the Greek word *theriaca*, meaning an antidote to animal bites. Mithridate is named after the legendary Mithridates VI of Pontus (*see the earlier Greek and Roman section*). Most of the *theriacas* and the various *mithridatium* or *mithridate* contained dozens of constituents, including exotic spices such as ginger, cinnamon, cassia, cardamon, nard, pepper, frankincense, myrrh and saffron. They took months to prepare and ferment. These mostly ineffective remedies remained in official use until the 19th century, giving rise to a host of similar tonics. Some of them even enjoy a wide market today.

VOYAGES OF DISCOVERY
AND EXPLORATION

Fifteenth century

The Ottoman Empire was the successor to the Roman and Byzantine empires. Constantinople, formerly the centre of Roman trade under Constantine, fell to the Turks in 1453. The spread of the Ottoman Empire made old land routes to the sources of silk and spices unsafe, so the need for a sea route to the Orient became more urgent than ever.

At the height of its power in the 16th and 17th centuries, the Empire spanned three continents, from southern Europe to the Middle East and North Africa. It stretched from the Straits of Gibraltar to the Caspian Sea and the Persian Gulf in the east and from the edge of Austria and parts of Ukraine in the north to Sudan and Yemen in the south. The centuries-old trade in spices described by Marco Polo was tightly controlled by this new empire, and the international trade that relied on spices was threatened. Europeans therefore had to find a new route to the spice lands, avoiding the Ottoman Empire. Explorers were sent out by ship into the unknown.

To cut a long story short, this led to the discovery of the New World as well as sea routes to the East Indies and Africa. During the 16th century the naval supremacy of the Ottomans was challenged by European countries like Portugal. The Ottomans blockaded sea routes to the east and south, but these were later bypassed. On land, wars in Austria and Persia put a strain on supply lines and the sea routes were lost. The port of Venice then lost its power over Mediterranean trade.

During the 15th century Portugal led the European world in sea exploration. The influence of this small country lasted almost a century until the Dutch eventually seized trade routes from them. The Portuguese were attempting to find a route around Africa into the Indian Ocean in order to trade directly with India and the Far East. During the previous century they had driven the Muslim Moors out of the parts of Portugal and Spain which had been controlled by them for centuries. In 1415 the Portuguese captured the city of Ceuta on the northern coast of Africa. From then on Portugal expanded its influence on the western coast of Africa in order to spread Christianity and increase trade. Overland routes to Asia were blocked by the Ottomans, so Portuguese mariners began to work their way down the coast of Africa in search of gold and trade routes to the East.

The man chiefly responsible for Portugal's age of exploration was Prince Henry the Navigator. From 1419 until his death in 1460 he sent expedition after expedition down the west coast of Africa to outflank the Muslim hold on trade routes and to establish colonies. Expeditions moved slowly, beset with rumours of boiling water at the equator, human skin turning black, and sea monsters engulfing ships.
In 1487 Bartholomew Diaz finally braved the dangers and rounded the Cape of Good Hope.

Meanwhile, Columbus was trying to get backers for his expedition to discover a westerly route to the Spice Islands. He believed that by sailing west, instead of east around the coast of Africa, he would reach the Spice Islands. Having got support from King Ferdinand and Queen Isabella of Spain, he set off in 1492. When land was spotted Columbus was convinced that it was an island off the coast of India, but when other islands came into view he named them the 'Indies'. These are now known as the West Indies. Still, although he didn't find the route to the East Indies, he had the discovery of the Americas as a consolation prize.

In 1497 King Manuel I of Portugal sent Vasco da Gama to follow the route previously taken by Diaz. He charted the waters and explored thousands of miles of coastline before reaching Mozambique. This was the southernmost African port under Arab control. He then continued to Calicut on the west coast of India, arriving in May 1498. This first voyage from Europe to the East, around Africa to India, was the most significant feat in the history of the spice trade.

Da Gama stayed in Calicut for nearly six months, returning to Lisbon in 1499, minus two-thirds of the crew who had died of scurvy. He brought with him precious stones and spices and a message from the Zamorin, the Hindu leader of Calicut, to King Manuel, apparently experiencing his pleasure at the arrival of Da Gama and describing a country rich in cloves, ginger, cinnamon, pepper and gemstones. He wished to exchange these for gold, silver, corals and scarlet cloth.

As a note of interest, when King Manuel seized the opportunity to add new colonies and trade to his kingdom, he dispatched 13 caravels to Calicut in March 1500, under the command of Pedro Alvarez Cabral. For some strange reason, Cabral sailed westward instead of south and landed in South America. Here he took possession of Brazil for Portugal before carrying on to Calicut. The Arab merchants were obviously not very happy about this, but despite the loss of four ships in storms and the massacre of 50 of his men, he returned the following year with a rich cargo of diamonds and pearls, and an assortment of spices – cinnamon, cassia, ginger, pepper, nutmegs, mace and cloves.

By 1511 the Portuguese had access to the Spice Islands. These islands, known as the Moluccas and now known as Indonesia, were the only economically viable source of cloves, mace and nutmeg at the time. Portugal's success and the establishment of its monopoly provoked the other European maritime powers of Spain, France, England and the Netherlands into action. These islands later became part of the Dutch East Indies empire. A direct sea passage to India led to a marked increase in the availability and consumption of spices throughout Europe.

Sixteenth- and seventeenth-century trading
Trade extended to China and Japan in 1513. Ginger was probably introduced to Japan more than 2,000 years ago from China. Once trade with Japan became more important, the Portuguese lost interest in the Spice Islands.

By 1560 overland trade routes to the Orient had been re-established. Substantial quantities of spices, about four-fifths of the total trade, reached Europe through Portuguese and Spanish ports. The rest came through Alexandria.

The New World
During the 16th and 17th centuries ginger plantings were successfully established in the West Indies with plants brought from the East Indies. Ginger was probably the easiest of the tropical spices to grow and its simple requirements soon led to large-scale

production. Sources credit Francisco de Mendosa with the introduction of cloves, pepper, ginger and other spices to the New World. He had a personal interest in herbs and spices, education of the indigenous people, and the demand of Europeans for herbs and spices. Santa Domingo, Jamaica and Barbados all grew the spice. In Jamaica ginger fumes or hot ginger tea were used to relieve head colds. Early Jamaican records apparently show that in 1547, 1,000 tons of ginger were exported from the West Indies to Europe. By 1585 Santa Domingo was also exporting the spice. Portuguese slaves cultivated ginger in West Africa and Brazil, and it became naturalised in America.

By the end of the 17th century the Dutch had crushed the Portuguese, almost driven the British out of the East Indies and gained complete control of the spice trade in nutmeg, mace, cloves, cinnamon, Indian pepper, ginger and turmeric.

Towards the end of the 18th century, after the American War of Independence, the USA began to enter the trade in spices. British taxes and trade restrictions no longer obstructed American commerce and the ships that had been built for war were available for peacetime assignments. American fish, tobacco, snuff, flour, soap, candles, butter, cheese and beef were traded for tea, coffee, textiles, indigo and spices, including ginger. Sugar and rum could be acquired in the West Indies. However, the most valuable trade was in spices.

Spice oils

An important development in spice processing came in 1899 with the introduction of ginger oil or oleoresin. Natural resins and volatile essential oils contain the constituents of flavour, smell and pungency of the spice in concentrated form, making it easier to transport. You can read more about this in a later section.

Figging

To end this chapter on a less savoury note, I must mention a less friendly use of ginger, called figging. This was a widespread practice before World War One, where horses were given ginger suppositories before parades or public ceremonies, in order to keep their tails high in the air. The ginger caused a burning sensation, so the poor horses obviously liked to keep their rears uncovered and the air circulating. I'd hate to be around when the ginger popped, or pooped, out!

What Does Ginger Consist Of?

WHAT DOES GINGER CONSIST OF?

Apart from its obvious benefits of taste and smell and the impact it has on various recipes, ginger has a lot more going for it in terms of nutrition and beneficial properties. Ginger has long been known to ease the symptoms of different ailments, but in more recent years scientific research has isolated some of the compounds that offer remedies. Nutritional experts have also studied the inclusion of ginger in a balanced diet in greater depth. Some of the identified components occur naturally and some are the result of processing. Health benefits are dealt with in detail in the next chapter.

Approximate nutritional contents of 100 g of fresh ginger
Of course, this is an estimate based on the findings from some types of unspecified ginger. Values will differ, depending on freshness, shelf-life and variety. Also bear in mind that most of these minerals are merely present in traces and that no one would normally eat 100 g of ginger at a time.

	Ginger rhizome, per 100 g
Calories	20
Carbohydrate	17.8 g (1.7 g sugar)
Protein	1.8 g
Fat	0.75 g
Fibre	2 g
Folate	11 microgram
Vitamin C	5 mg
Vitamin B6	0.16 mg
Magnesium	43 mg
Calcium	16 mg
Sodium	3.7 mg
Phosphorus	34 mg
Iron	0.6 mg
Niacin	0.75 mg
Potassium	415 mg
Thiamine	0.025 mg
Riboflavin	0.03 mg
Pantothenic acid	0.2 mg
Water	23 g
Zinc	0.34 mg

Traces of omega 3 fatty acid and omega 6 are also present.

AN A TO Z OF SOME OF THE NUTRIENTS AND BENEFICIAL COMPOUNDS FOUND IN GINGER

This section gives some background information on minerals, vitamins and other identified compounds that may be found in ginger, as well as a lot of other naturally good foods.

Anthocyanins

These are a type of flavonoid which is prevalent in the pigment of a variety of plants, fruit and vegetables. Anthocyanin is the pigment responsible for making red cabbage different from other varieties and is present in some varieties of fresh ginger, but not all. Japanese ginger is said to contain anthocyanins but there is variation between different plants and where they are cultivated. Two types of anthocyanin were isolated from ginger rhizomes by chromatography methods. These were only present in the lower stem and rhizome of the ginger plant.

When ginger is in contact with an acidic substance, like vinegar, the anthocyanin turns bright pink, giving the ginger root a pinkish hue. This is used in Japanese pickled ginger to good effect, without using pink or red food colouring.

Gingerols

These are what gives ginger its pungency and are thought to be useful in treating fever and pain.
The volatile oils may kill cold and flu viruses.
They may also reduce nausea caused by motion sickness or pregnancy and migraine. Researchers in India found that gingerol increased bile production, showing that it helps in digestion and absorption of food. Research has also shown that gingerol can slow

the growth of tumours in mice. Cooking turns gingerol into zingerone (*see below*). Studies have shown that gingerols have a similar structure to capsaicin, the active ingredient of chilli peppers and capsicum, which is a known pain reliever. It is normally found as a pungent yellow oil.

Iron
Iron is found in every cell in the body. Iron links with protein to form haemoglobin, which is the oxygen transporter in your blood. Iron keeps your immune system healthy and helps to produce energy. Insufficient iron leads to anaemia.

Magnesium
This helps to regulate the nerve and muscle tone. Magnesium keeps the muscles relaxed by preventing calcium entering the nerve cells. Insufficient magnesium may lead to muscle spasms or cramps, migraine, high blood pressure and fatigue. Magnesium, calcium and phosphorus function together in bone formation, muscle contraction, and nerve transmission. Ginger is quite high in these minerals.

Oils and oleoresins
Ginger oil is extracted commercially by steam distillation of dried powdered ginger. The yield varies from 1 per cent to 3 per cent. Most of the ginger oil is used as a flavouring agent for alcoholic and non-alcoholic drinks.

Ginger oil can be produced from fresh or dried rhizomes, although oil from dried rhizomes will contain fewer of the volatile compounds that give ginger its flavour and aroma. The best ginger oil is obtained from whole, unpeeled rhizomes.

Ginger oil is obtained using a process of steam distillation. The dried rhizomes are ground to a coarse powder and loaded into a still. Steam is passed through the powder, which extracts the volatile oil components. The steam is then condensed with cold water. As the steam condenses, the oils separate out of the steam water and can be collected. In India the material is re-distilled to get the maximum yield of oil. The yield of oil from dried ginger rhizomes is between 1.5 per cent to 3.0 per cent. The remaining rhizome powder contains about 50 per cent starch and can be used for animal feed. It is sometimes dried and ground to make an inferior spice.

An oleoresin is a mixture of oil containing turpentine and a resin. Now before we all get the wrong idea and get confused with solvents and paint strippers, we are talking medically here. Turpentine was originally distilled from pine trees and particularly from the terebinth tree. You may or may not be interested to know that turpentine is a highly effective treatment for lice and internal parasites and was used with animal fat as a chest rub and for nose and throat problems. Some modern products still contain it. It is not normally taken internally today.

Medicinally, an oleoresin is a preparation extracted from plants like capsicums (or peppers) and ginger. The oil holds the resins in solution. The oleoresin in ginger rhizomes contains oils and pungent compounds which can be extracted with solvents such as acetone or alcohol.

The volatile oil components in ginger consist predominantly of zingeberene (about 35 per cent), curcumene (18 per cent) and farnesene (10 per cent). An alcohol known as zingiberol has also been isolated.

Many of these constituents together help to create ginger's distinctive aroma and taste. Most are not, however, unique to ginger.

Oleoresins are products obtained by extraction of the spice by solvents. These solvents are then removed. The spice may contain from between 3 per cent and 30 per cent by weight of oleoresin, although the average is about 10 per cent.

Some of the ginger produced under tropical conditions — and which may become contaminated by mould and bacteria — can still be used for the extraction of oleoresins, even if the spice cannot be eaten. Oleoresin from ginger is usually obtained by extraction from dried powdered ginger with organic solvents like ethyl acetate or ethanol. Ginger oleoresin is a dark brown viscous liquid. Some of the oleoresins are used in the canning and frozen food industries.

Phosphorus
Phosphorus is a mineral that makes up 1 per cent of the total body weight. It is present in every cell of the body, but 85 per cent of the body's phosphorus is found in the bones and teeth. It plays an important role in the body's use of carbohydrates and fats, and in the synthesis of protein for the growth, maintenance and repair of cells and tissues. It is also crucial for the production of a molecule the body uses to store energy.

Phosphorus works with the B vitamins. It assists in the contraction of muscles, in kidney function, in maintaining the regularity of the heartbeat, and in nerve conduction. A meal plan that provides adequate amounts of calcium and protein also provides an adequate amount of phosphorus.

Potassium

Potassium helps all the muscles in the body to contract. It is essential for heart function and maintaining normal blood pressure. Studies have shown that potassium reduces blood pressure and the risk of strokes. So eating ginger may help to protect the body against bone fragility, muscle weakness, mental apathy and confusion, and damage to the heart. In addition to potassium's role in blood pressure regulation, it also regulates heartbeat.

Shogaols

These aromatic compounds are a type of gingerol (*see above*). Shogaols are formed as ginger ages, while gingerols degrade. The highest concentrations of shogaols occur in dried ginger. Both shogaols and other gingerols seem to have a positive effect on the heart, possibly by accelerating the take-up of calcium. They inhibit the formation of prostaglandins, which are hormone-like substances that function in the contraction and relaxation of muscle and the dilation and constriction of blood vessels. Some migraine sufferers have reported relief by taking ginger at the onset; the theory being that inflammation of blood vessels, which causes pain, is reduced. See the next section for more details.

The Vitamin B group

Vitamin B1 (thiamin)

Thiamin is one of a group of water-soluble vitamins that participate in many of the chemical reactions in the body. Thiamin helps the body cells convert carbohydrates into energy. It is also essential for the functioning of the heart, muscles and nervous system. A deficiency in thiamin can cause weakness, fatigue, psychosis and nerve damage. A high consumption of alcohol makes it hard for the body to absorb thiamin from foods.

Vitamin B2 *(riboflavin)*

Riboflavin has a number of important functions. It helps keep skin, eyes, the nervous system and mucous membranes healthy. It may help the body absorb iron from the food we eat and it helps produce steroids and red blood cells.

Vitamin B3 *(niacin)*

Niacin helps the body turn the food we eat into energy. It also helps keep the nervous and digestive systems healthy.

Vitamin B5 *(pantothenic acid)*

Ginger contains small amounts of this important vitamin; it is the key to metabolism of carbohydrates, fats and proteins. In combination with zinc, it is claimed that B5 can prevent hair from turning grey in rats. It can promote resistance to the stress of cold immersion and may be tied to tumour inhibition. In combination with vitamin C it maintains capillary walls and promotes circulation. It is also said to be antibacterial and to promote pain relief.

Vitamin B6 *(pyridoxine)*

Pyridoxine is water-soluble. It is required for both mental and physical health. It is needed for balancing hormonal changes in women, assisting the immune system and the growth of new cells. It is also used in the processing of proteins, fats and carbohydrates. It helps to control mood and behaviour. Pyridoxine is also thought to be of benefit to children with learning difficulties, as well as assisting in the prevention of skin complaints. It helps to promote red blood cell production and has been linked to cancer immunity and prevention of heart disease.

Vitamin B9 (folate, or folic acid)
Folate is the naturally occurring form of folic acid, the name of the synthetic form. It is necessary for the production and maintenance of new cells, especially important during periods of rapid cell division and growth, such as during pregnancy and infancy, but everyone needs folate to make normal red blood cells and prevent anaemia. Folic acid is topical at present, as research advises women to take folic acid supplements for a year before becoming pregnant. This is said to reduce the risk of premature births by 70%. Medication that interferes with the body's ability to use folate may also increase the need for this vitamin. In the USA, folic acid has been added to bread and flour since 1998 and there is a growing call for it to be added in the UK as well. Foods that are rich in folate include strawberries, citrus fruit and leafy green vegetables. Ground ginger has more folate per 100g than fresh ginger.

Vitamin C
Vitamin C is the main water-soluble antioxidant in the body and is vital for the healthy functioning of the immune system. It is good at preventing common colds and may also help to reduce recurrent ear infections. It is essential for healthy teeth and gums, helps wounds to heal, helps fractures to mend and heals scar tissue. Deficiency led to scurvy amongst sailors in the past.

Vitamin C helps vitamin E become active and is associated with reducing inflammation caused by asthma and arthritis. It is also particularly effective in combating free-radical formation caused by pollution and cigarette smoke.

Zingerone

Zingerone gives ginger its pungent taste. It is a crystalline solid. It forms when gingerol is cooked and is used as a flavour additive in spice oils. Zingerone is also used in perfumery, to introduce spicy-sweet aromas that are less pungent.

Zingibain

Zingibain is an enzyme in ginger that has anti-inflammatory properties, along with many other antioxidants.

Zingiberene

Zingiberene is the predominant constituent of the oil of ginger, accounting for 20% to 30% of the volatile oil. It functions as an insecticide or repellent. Interestingly, the same compound has been found in the leaves of wild tomatoes.

Zingiberol

This is another of the volatile oils that have been isolated in ginger. Ginger oil does not give off a peppery sensation, but zingiberol is an alcohol with the fragrance of ginger.

Medicinal
Uses

BENEFITS TO HEALTH AND WELL-BEING FROM GINGER

If you've read the section on historical uses of ginger you won't be surprised to learn that ginger has been used for thousands of years in Asia to treat a range of illnesses and ailments. More recently, research has shown how and why many of these applications work and the use of ginger has gained credibility. This section brings together folk remedies, ancient and modern, as well as some more recent innovations. Some of them may seem a little strange or unlikely, and their inclusion does not mean that they are recommended. As always, if in doubt, seek proper medical advice rather than relying solely on the following information.

Ginger is used in nearly half of the prescriptions in Chinese medicine, in combination with many other herbs. Sometimes it is used to counter the effects of other ingredients or to stimulate the appetite and/or calm the stomach. Ginger is described as a carrier herb, namely one that can enhance the absorption of other herbs and make them more effective.

The main benefits of the use of ginger seem to be in alleviating stomach disorders and as an anti-inflammatory, antioxidant agent, but there are many more. Herbal medicine regards ginger as an excellent carminative, which means that it is good at getting rid of gas from the intestines. It also relaxes and soothes the intestinal tract.

Some remedies incorporate other members of the ginger family, such as galangal, zedoary, cardamom and turmeric (*see Chapter 1*). Galanga, and zedoary taken together are said to be a cure for stomach ailments in many Arab countries, although they have been replaced largely by ginger in other parts of the world today. Combined together, they are considered stimulants and aphrodisiacs. Another claim suggests that they can cure amnesia, but I don't recall having heard about that! Combined with olive oil, they make a body rub to ease muscle complaints.

Wise precautions

Herbs often contain components that can trigger side effects and interact with other herbs or medications. For these reasons, take care when under medical supervision or taking prescribed drugs. Side effects are said to be rare, although if taken in excessive amounts ginger may cause mild heartburn. People with gallstones and those about to undergo surgery, or be anaesthetised, should consult a doctor before taking ginger. Likewise, do not take ginger if you are taking blood-thinning medications, including aspirin. Importantly, ginger is not a recommended treatment for children under the age of two years.

POSSIBLE BENEFITS TO HEALTH FROM EATING GINGER

ANTI-INFLAMMATORY EFFECTS

As we saw in the previous chapter, ginger contains compounds called gingerols and shogaols. These are strong anti-inflammatory compounds and seem to account for the fact that many people with osteoarthritis or rheumatoid arthritis consume ginger regularly to gain relief. The results reported include reductions in pain levels and improvements in mobility.

Arthritis

Clinical studies involving patients with arthritis and muscular discomfort found that three in four arthritis patients and all patients with muscular discomfort experienced relief from pain and/or swelling. Patients with arthritis in the knee, ranging in age from 40–85 years, participated in a study where they switched from placebo to ginger or vice versa after three months. After six months those given ginger were experiencing significantly less pain than those given a placebo. Those who were switched from ginger to a placebo experienced an increase in pain. When all patients were taking ginger, pain remained low and swelling lessened (identified by measuring knee circumference). I pity the poor people who had to cope with a placebo for three months at a time!

In a larger study of over 250 people with osteoarthritis of the knees, patients given ginger extract twice per day needed fewer painkillers than those who received a placebo. On the other hand, one study found that ginger was no more effective than ibuprofen. Still, if you can't take anti-inflammatory painkillers, ginger might be worth a try. To relieve arthritis pain, take freshly squeezed ginger juice or ginger tea; 2–4 grams daily should be enough. Ginger oil may also be rubbed into a painful joint. Another method is to make a warm compress (*see below*) and apply to painful areas.

Galangal

Another study of more than 250 participants found that a combination of ginger and galangal, another plant similar to ginger, can significantly improve arthritis symptoms. However, the study did not draw any conclusions on the effectiveness of the ginger component over the galangal.

A study from 2003 suggests that gingerol offers free radical protection. Gingerol has been shown to significantly inhibit the production of nitric oxide, which quickly forms a very damaging, nasty free radical called peroxynitrite.

Another study in 2003 found that mice that were given five-day treatments with ginger before exposure to radiation experienced no increase in free radical damage to lipids or fats and a lessened depletion of glutathione, an antioxidant.

Turmeric

Glucosamine is said to help arthritis sufferers by stimulating the body's ability to manufacture glycosaminoglycan. This helps the cartilage retain its shock-absorbing ability. A spice that combines well with glucosamine is turmeric, a member of the ginger family. They work better together as a team than either substance does separately, to strengthen cartilage and reduce pain and inflammation.

APHRODISIACAL QUALITIES

The aphrodisiacal powers of ginger have some philosophical and scientific medical backing, although its reputation has also been enhanced through various myths and legends. Ginger has often been credited with increasing attraction, lust and the feeling of love, as well as stimulating sex drive and increasing sexual energy. In Asia ginger has been considered an aphrodisiac for centuries. Ginger can be applied internally or externally. The mind boggles, but I think the external application is part of a recipe for massage oil. Maybe it was the galangal, zedoary and olive oil rub. Some women in Senegal wear belts of ginger roots to get their men in the mood.

Stimulating

Ginger is mentioned in the *Kama Sutra*, the ancient Indian text on love and sexual behaviour. The qualities are associated with ginger's aroma and its scent is recognised by many as a sexual stimulant. Ginger increases circulation, which is thought to make erogenous zones hypersensitive. Another reason why ginger is considered an aphrodisiac is because ginger makes people sweat. Warming of the body increases perspiration, which, in turn, increases heart rate. These symptoms are similar to the body's reactions during sex. I just love the smell of fresh ginger, myself.

Mad for it

The Greeks and Romans of the 1st century AD, such as Dioscorides and Pliny, agreed with the widely held view that ginger had a stimulating effect on the male sexual organ. You can read more about these physicians in Chapter 2. Perhaps it was no coincidence, then, that the Romans were mad for spices and perfumes to enhance their decadent, somewhat hedonistic lifestyle. Interestingly, some recent fragrance testing claims to have discovered that the scent of fresh ginger could be detected in very dilute forms: allegedly one part to 35,000, compared with powdered ginger, at one part to 1,750.

Lustful yearnings

The aesthetic moods identified as tranquil, reclusive, luxurious, beautiful, refined or noble by the ancient Chinese also gave room for ginger as an aphrodisiacal fragrance, when jasmine oils were mixed with cloves, ginger and other perfumed compounds to fragrance dance performances, baths, cosmetics and clothing. Perhaps the spice trade was about more than just enhancing food. Aviceena (AD 980–1038) is considered one of the greatest names in Arabian medicine. He thought that ginger was capable of 'increasing lustful yearnings'. Ginger is also mentioned in the Koran, the sacred writings of Islam, as being served at feasts in Paradise.

Omelette, darling?

In 18th-century France Madame du Barry served ginger to all her lovers. She was the official royal mistress to King Louis XV from 1769 until his death in 1774. Mind you, she also served them cups of chocolate, but that's another story. Legend suggests that her recipe for feeding her men a sort of ginger omelette would drive her men to a state of complete and utter submissiveness. I have my money on the chocolate (*see the recipe section*)!

Racy rats

In 2002 a study looked at the effects of ginger on rats. For eight days the rats were given ginger-infused droplets of water, in order to test their testosterone levels. The rats experienced an increase in the weight of the testes and in testosterone levels. I don't imagine it did the poor rats much good in the long run, though.

Poor slaves

Rather more unpleasantly, one source suggests that the myth of aphrodisiacal qualities actually encouraged Portuguese slave traders to feed their slaves the spice in West Africa, in the hope of increasing the number of slaves in their grasp and, in turn, their profits.

CANCER TREATMENTS

Some US research suggests that gingerols, as well as offering pain and inflammation relief, may also inhibit the growth of cancer cells. Mice with no immune system were fed gingerol three times a week before being injected with cancer cells. The details of this research are fairly unpleasant, but the outcome offers encouragement to cancer research. Some mice (control group) were not given gingerol and they developed tumours after a couple of weeks. The main group started to develop tumours after two weeks, although at only 25 per cent of the rate of the control group. After seven weeks there were significantly smaller tumours present.

Other research on ovarian cancer has used ginger extract containing 5 per cent gingerol. The gingerol was seen to kill the cancer cells. In the presence of ginger, a number of key indicators of inflammation, including prostaglandins, were also decreased in the ovarian cancer cells. Chemotherapy also suppresses inflammatory markers, but may cause cancer cells to become resistant to the action of the drugs.

It is claimed that ginger may be of special benefit for ovarian cancer patients because cells exposed to ginger do not become resistant to its cancer-destroying effects. UK cancer experts say that, while ginger may form a basis of a new drug in the future, more research is needed. The appeal has to be because ginger has virtually no side effects and is easily administered as a capsule. Because of the anti-nausea effects that ginger offers to patients and its ability to help with dry, sore mouth conditions which many cancer patients suffer from, ginger is suggested by cancer charities as a safe treatment for side effects of chemotherapy.

Related to ginger, turmeric is another spice that has been shown to have many therapeutic uses. Research in Malaysia into the properties of turmeric (*Curcuma domestica*) extracts found that turmeric completely inhibited further growth of cancer cells in rats.

CIRCULATION

The therapeutic properties of ginger include the ability to stimulate the circulatory system. Ginger also appears to remove toxins, helps to clean the bowels and kidneys and nourish the skin. The increase in blood circulation helps to stimulate other areas of the body as well, like the hands and feet. Ginger is used for the treatment of chilblains by helping to increase the blood circulation at the surface level of the skin.

Ginger is also thought to help in controlling blood pressure, as it directly affects the circulation of blood, but more research is needed to corroborate this claim.

It is also too early to tell whether ginger will benefit those with heart disease, although a few studies have suggested that ginger may lower cholesterol and prevent the blood from clotting. These effects may protect the blood vessels from blockage or the damaging effects of a blockage such as atherosclerosis. This is a disease affecting arterial blood vessels, with chronic inflammation due to the deposition of plasma proteins that carry cholesterol, commonly referred to as a hardening of the arteries. It can lead to a heart attack or stroke.

Many patients are recommended by their doctors to take a daily aspirin to remedy this build-up. Some researchers in 1980 found ginger to be as effective as aspirin in this respect and other studies have supported this finding since. In addition, it was found that ginger's antioxidant properties strengthened cardiac muscle. Studies in Japan and India have claimed that ginger lowers serum cholesterol levels.

Because ginger may have blood thinning and cholesterol lowering properties, it should not be taken with aspirin or when taking prescribed anti-coagulant drugs.

COLDS, TEMPERATURES AND FEVER
Nigerian herbal practitioners use ginger for the treatment of malaria and yellow fever. Hopefully, there's not much call for that here. Sweating is increased by remedies made from ginger but at the same time, the herb can assist in lowering a fever. It can alleviate chills caused by colds as it warms the body. The antibacterial and antiviral effects of ginger may help reduce the incidence of colds altogether.

I always remember being made to stay in bed when I had a cold and flu-like symptoms as a child, with plenty of blankets to make me 'sweat it out'. This isn't perhaps the suggested remedy nowadays, as high temperatures in children can be another problem, but

I suppose ginger can be warming on a cold day and can help relieve aching joints. A good sweat may also assist detoxification.

DIGESTION
Ginger is most commonly known for its effectiveness as an aid to digestion. It increases the production of digestive fluids and saliva and thereby helps relieve indigestion, wind pains, diarrhoea and stomach cramping. Gingerols increase bile production and absorption of food. For this reason, people suffering from gallstones should avoid ginger, as the herb helps to release bile from the gallbladder.

If food is digested more efficiently, any unfriendly bacteria have less chance of causing problems that could keep you visiting the loo more frequently than you would like. Along these lines, chemicals in ginger have been proven to knock out the sort of bacteria that cause upsets. One of the classic treatments for bacterial dysentery in the tropics, is ginger. Zingibain in ginger seems to enhance other antibacterials such as antibiotics. Some claims have been made that ginger can effectively treat certain types of food poisoning as well.

NAUSEA AND VOMITING
I can think of at least three periods in my life when I would have jumped at the chance of eating ginger to relieve nausea. If only I had known, I would have exchanged the digestive biscuits for ginger snaps. Two of these were pregnancies, where the morning sickness went on for months . . . and months.
The other was when suffering from Hepatitis A as a teenager. The only treatment I was given then was to suck travel sickness pills. Funnily enough, I have never suffered from motion sickness.

Ginger has long been used, apparently to provide relief from nausea and vomiting. Ginger root is used to treat nausea related to both motion sickness and morning sickness and has been found to be even more effective than commercial drugs in curbing motion sickness, without causing drowsiness. While most anti-nausea drugs work on the brain and the inner ear, ginger acts directly on the stomach.

For the treatment of nausea, some people have gained relief from taking approximately 250 mg every two to three hours, up to a total of 1 gram per day.

Morning sickness

Many women find that ginger eases morning sickness. In India women regularly eat quantities of ginger during pregnancy, with few side effects it seems. In Chinese medicine, women are advised to be careful in using ginger, especially at the beginning of their pregnancy. This may be due, however, to the large amounts recommended, where up to 9 g of fresh root may be used in a remedy per dose. Trials in the West only used 1 g per dose, and many studies have shown that some women suffering from morning sickness respond well to ginger. If you don't like the taste, there may be a problem, of course, and tastes do tend to change when you are pregnant.

In several studies between 50 per cent and 75 per cent of women found that ginger eased their nausea, although the response was different in each of the women. Some women found that symptoms went away all together when using ginger, whilst others found that the nausea eased when taking it.

A study in Australia was carried out on 120 women who were less than 20 weeks pregnant, had suffered from morning sickness for more than a week and had not managed to gain relief from other dietary changes. They were given 125 mg of ginger extract, the equivalent to 1.5 g of dried rhizome, four times a day for four days. One group was given a placebo. The nausea was significantly less for the ginger extract group after the first day of treatment. There was no significant effect observed on those unfortunates who vomited, but who wants to be observed vomiting anyway? Four women suffered reflux and heartburn caused by the high dose of ginger used.

A second Australian study measured the effect of a daily dose of 1.05 g of ginger or 75 mg of vitamin B6 (pyridoxine). The treatment was given for three weeks and the trial found that ginger was equivalent to vitamin B6 in reducing nausea, retching and vomiting. Well, ginger contains very small amounts of pyridoxine, so maybe there's something else to try. It can be found in a number of foods as well as supplements that also contain ginger.

Overall, it seems that ginger can help women cope with the sickening feelings that many experience during the first three months of pregnancy. Because root ginger is a natural product there should not be a problem, but if you take supplements or capsules with other ingredients always check for other substances. If in doubt, ask a professional.

Motion sickness
Ginger has long been used for those who suffer from nausea due to motion sickness. A fun-sounding study of 80 Scandinavian naval cadets found that 1 g of ginger could decrease vomiting and cold sweating. They still felt nauseous and suffered vertigo, however.

They must have looked drunk. There's a song title there somewhere . . .

A study funded by NASA during the 1980s simulated motion sickness in a lab. It was found that ginger was no more effective than a placebo, although the reason may have related to the type of ginger used, or the severity of the stimulant used to induce motion sickness. Most people don't have to deal with motion sickness caused by space travel, after all.

A study in London in 1990 suggested that ginger seems to be more effective than some standard drugs in treating motion sickness and dizziness. Volunteers who took ginger were able to endure artificially created seasickness 57 per cent longer than those who used a prescription drug. The simulation involved using a mechanical rocking chair. How unpleasant!

There is a suggestion that to prevent motion sickness, you might need to start taking ginger a day or two before the trip and continue it throughout the period of travel in the form of ginger tablets, capsules or liquid herbal extract. That's fine if you have plenty of warning that you need to travel, of course.

Conventional medicines that decrease nausea often cause unwanted side effects, such as a dry mouth and drowsiness, so given that ginger is safe to use, many people may find it a welcome alternative.

Other forms of nausea
Ginger root is widely used as a digestive aid for mild stomach upsets.

A few studies have suggested that ginger reduces the severity and duration of nausea during chemotherapy, although it doesn't stop vomiting. Long-term studies need to be undertaken to confirm these results and to establish safety.

A British study followed 120 women receiving gynaecological surgery. Only 21 per cent who took ginger reported nausea and vomiting whereas 41 per cent of the participants given a placebo had these symptoms. However, another study found no benefit was derived from taking ginger, so if ginger is effective for post-surgical nausea at all, the effect is thought to be slight.

PAIN RELIEF
The anti-inflammatory relief from the gingerols has been described above. Other causes of pain may also be alleviated.

Period pain
Medical researchers today think that an imbalance of prostaglandins causes the pain associated with menstruation. Prostaglandins (which participate in muscle contraction and dilation of blood vessels) in the lining of the uterus may be responsible for the cramping sensation in the uterine muscles. Pain relievers like aspirin and ibuprofen inhibit the synthesis of prostaglandins. Herbs traditionally used for painful periods contain constituents that also inhibit prostaglandins and ginger is one of these. It contains at least eight such constituents, including gingerols, shogaols, curcumin and quercetin. These help to relax the muscles in the walls of blood vessels and reduce pressure.

Headache and migraine
A headache cure in India is to paste the temples with ginger. As I said in the previous paragraph, the

gingerols and shogaols help to reduce pressure on blood vessels and relax muscles, thus having a calming effect on headaches. The anti-nausea effects may help with migraine attacks.

ULCERS
Research comparing the use of ginger with prescription drugs found that they both reduced irritation to the digestive tract. The drugs, however, only suppressed the problem, whereas the ginger has a balancing function. This allows it to protect while it inhibits toxic bacteria, enabling friendly bacteria to grow. The ulcer may be caused by an infection in the system, so ginger, with its anti-inflammatory qualities and ability to fight bacteria, may play a helpful role. Care should be taken, however, not to exacerbate the ulcer by consuming too much ginger.

OTHER HEALTH CLAIMS
AND FOLK CURES

Ginger has been considered a universal medicinal herb for centuries. Chinese medicine lists similar primary uses of ginger as other types of medicine, but additionally suggests using ginger for haemorrhages, kidney problems, paralysis and sinus problems. Chinese sailors are said to have eaten ginger for its vitamin C content, to keep scurvy at bay, although there isn't a lot of vitamin C in ginger.

It has been used in India to treat a range of ailments because of its antiseptic, digestive and stimulant qualities. Many people believe that it can affect part of the central nervous system and can effectively treat vertigo as well as nausea. The following additional complaints have also cited the use of ginger. Some are more familiar than others to Western medicine:

Asthma

Backache

Bronchitis

Breast cancer

Diarrhoea

Dog bites

Malaria

Scorpion stings

Syphilis

Tetanus

Toothache

Elsewhere in the world, ginger is used for the following:

ATHLETE'S FOOT
Ginger contains antifungal compounds, so it can be administered to affected areas in a concoction twice a day. Add about 25 g (1 oz) to a cup of boiling water and let it steep for 20 minutes before applying with cotton wool.

BAD BREATH
Chewing ginger is said to be a good mouth and breath freshener. The antibiotic properties probably see to that, and may cover up other odours, like garlic.

BODY ODOUR
The antibacterial qualities of ginger tea have been suggested for deodorising the armpits using a cloth. A shower sounds like a better idea.

DANDRUFF
Applied to the scalp three times a week, ginger oil, lemon juice and sesame oil have been recommended for this complaint. Mix 1 or 2 tablespoons of ginger juice with 3 tablespoons of sesame oil and ½ teaspoon lemon juice. It isn't clear when you should apply this, however. Presumably, in mid-wash or before washing the hair.

DEPRESSION
Ginger tea has been used as a treatment for mild depression and anxiety. See below for ginger tea.

HERBAL TONICS
In Indonesia, ginger is used as a herbal preparation to reduce fatigue, by reducing 'winds' in the blood. It is also used for rheumatism and controlling poor dietary habits.

The Democratic Republic of the Congo has a drink called ginger Tangawisi, made from crushed ginger mixed with mango-tree sap. The juice is considered a universal panacea.

In the Philippines a traditional breakfast drink called salabat is made by boiling chopped ginger and adding sugar.

HIVES
Rashes caused by food allergies have been treated with ginger in a bath. Boil 225 g (8 oz) of fresh ginger in water and add to a bath. Have a good soak and then rinse with chamomile tea.

FATIGUE
Some sufferers of Chronic Fatigue Syndrome and Fibromyalgia Syndrome have sought relief from ginger. Devotees of using ginger to treat illness say that fresh ginger, which is high in gingerol, and powdered ginger, high in shogaol, will have different effects. The strong antioxidants and benefits to circulation of ginger may be helpful. Side effects from ginger are said to be minimal, unless very high doses like 6,000 mg of dried ginger on an empty stomach are taken. This can cause stomach problems. One sufferer suggests adding about a 1 in cube of ginger to a smoothie or fruit juice two or three times a day.

PARASITES
Ginger extract has been found to immobilise over 90 per cent of larvae carried in fish within 4 hours and destroy them within 16 hours. Other claims suggest that ginger can kill parasites like worms by digesting their eggs.

RESPIRATORY DISORDERS

Other uses for ginger root include the treatment of asthma, bronchitis and other respiratory problems, by loosening and expelling phlegm from the lungs. Herbal remedies made from the ginger have a warming and soothing effect and help alleviate persistent coughs and colds. The remedies made from ginger have a stimulating effect and expectorant action inside the lungs. This is also thought to help relieve catarrh and sinus problems.

In Burma, ginger and a local sweetener made from palm tree juice are boiled together and taken in the hope of preventing flu. Similarly, in China, a drink made with sliced ginger cooked in sweetened water is used to treat the common cold.

RECIPES FOR HERBAL REMEDIES WITH GINGER

In Chinese and traditional oriental medicine, four different forms of ginger are identified in treatments and considered different medications. Fresh, dried, steamed and roasted ginger are said to have different values. However, analyses of the different forms do not appear to have found a wide variation in the elements they contain. It is known that fresh and dried ginger show differing levels of gingerols and, specifically, shogaols, but opinion is divided over whether one form is better than another.

Chinese medicine suggests the use of fresh ginger for promoting sweating, the treatment of fevers, headaches and nausea, and to alleviate aching muscles in the body. Dried ginger is used for the treatment of colds, clammy hands, constipation, urinary problems, a weakened pulse rate, and a pale complexion.

Personally, I always like to add fresh ginger to my cooking and try to include ginger as often as possible in soups, chicken dishes and stir-fries, along with garlic, onions, limes and lemons. My dietary needs are not helped by processed foods or salt, so these additions, along with pepper, compensate for salty sauces and ready made soups. The powerful smell and taste of fresh ginger just makes me feel healthy! Powdered ginger is what I use in cakes and biscuits, so ginger finds its way into lots of meals.

How much is too much? It is recommended that around 2–4 g daily in your diet is enough. Doses vary according to who you consult and the nature of the problem, so the suggestions below are just that. It is not recommended that children below the age of two years are given ginger. Older children will need to have doses reduced. Better still, ask a professional.

GINGER TEAS
Basic ginger tea
Ginger tea as a general pick-me-up can be made by simmering approximately ½–1 teaspoon of freshly grated ginger or approximately 2 teaspoons of dried ginger in about 150 ml (5 fl oz) of boiling water for about 10 minutes. Strain the tea before drinking it. Ginger tea can be sweetened with honey or sugar, or flavoured with other spices such as cinnamon.

For nausea, this may be too strong, so reduce the ginger and sip the tea to settle your stomach. This can be taken hot, cooled or even iced.

For arthritis relief doses vary, but two suggestions are to drink ½ teaspoon of powdered ginger in a cup of hot water daily, or use 6 teaspoons of fresh spice in a cup of boiling water. That sounds like rather a lot of ginger to me!

Lemon, ginger and honey tea
Peel and slice a piece of ginger about 4–6 cm long (1–2 in) into a mug and add boiling water. Add a teaspoon of honey and a good squeeze of fresh lemon juice. This is good for colds and sore throats.

Spicy fennel, ginger and cinnamon tea
Add ½ teaspoon of ginger powder, fennel seeds and cinnamon with a pinch of clove powder to a mug of hot water. Let the spices infuse for about 10 minutes, then strain and serve. I'm not sure what this is supposed to help.

Commercial teas

Chinese *Pu-erh* tea is widely thought to aid digestion, reduce cholesterol and lipid levels. The tea is used in traditional Chinese medicine, to invigorate the spleen, and some claims have been made regarding weight loss. *Pu-erh* tea can also be purchased combined with ginger and cloves. It is drunk to get rid of grease and toxins from a rich diet.

Another blend of ginger and orange peel, combined with *Pu-erh* tea, was inspired by 16th-century Chinese herbal doctors. It is said to improve digestion. Since tea is thought to be rich in antioxidants (along with red wine) there may be some benefit to be gained from such a combination.

Tulsi tea (holy basil tea) is an Indian tea combining Indian ginger with basil. It is caffeine-free and originated thousands of years ago. It is full of antioxidants and said to reduce stress.

COMPRESSES

Ginger is used in many herbal remedies to make a hot compress, but make sure it is fresh ginger.

Headache compress

At the very basic level, a headache cure in India uses crushed fresh ginger, placed on the forehead. A simpler way is to add a few drops of ginger oil to some water. Soak a flannel or cloth in the bowl and use as a compress.

Swelling and cramps

A ginger compress can be effective in treating muscular stiffness, swollen joints and inflammation. Use the ginger oil or crushed ginger in hot water. The compress can be applied to the chest or stomach with a flannel (not too hot!) for coughs, colds or the relief of stomach cramps.

HONEY-GINGER SYRUP

Combining ginger with honey gives a double whammy effect as an antibacterial remedy. This can be especially comforting, if you don't like the taste of ginger that much. It can be taken warm or cold. Add one part freshly grated ginger to three parts honey. Add 1 teaspoon per cup of hot water for colds. If you prefer something cold and fizzy, mix with carbonated mineral water to make a sort of ginger ale.

MASSAGE OIL

Add 5–10 drops ginger oil to 25 ml (1 fl oz) almond oil for rheumatism or lumbago. You could also use juniper or eucalyptus oil instead of almond oil.

FLATULENCE

This is apparently a French remedy, although I haven't come across it before. Use one or two drops of ginger oil on a sugar lump or in ½ teaspoon of honey. This is said to be good for flatulence, and also for menstrual cramps, nausea and stomach upsets. Now I know what all those sugar lumps are for in France.

HEALTHY TONICS

You can make healthy, tasty drinks yourself and add some fresh ginger to the daily diet. Ginger can be added to different fruit and vegetable juices, such as daily glasses of carrot or apple juice. Just don't go too mad at once: introduce the flavour gradually.

Fruit cocktail

Bananas, pineapple, blueberries, fresh or ground ginger and honey can be combined in various combinations to give a healthy drink. Use the honey sparingly and dilute with mineral water, if you like. See the recipe section for more ideas.

Stomach settlers

Ginger ale and ginger beer have been recommended as stomach settlers for generations. Be aware, however, that the active ginger ingredients are negligible in this form.

Cooking with Ginger

COOKING WITH GINGER

Ginger is one of those extremely versatile spices that can be used in all manner of dishes, both savoury and sweet. The possibilities seem endless and my 'problem' has been where to draw the line in compiling uses for cooking. As well as the more obvious Indian and Chinese traditional uses and good old gingerbread, there are many other ways in which to incorporate this beneficial spice into everyday dishes. It has become a regular addition to home-made soups in our house, along with lemon, since it cuts out the need for salt, as well as adding a unique flavour.

PURCHASING ROOT GINGER
If you have a choice, go for roots that have a firm, smooth skin with a light sheen. Avoid the shrivelled, broken pieces which may have been around longer, or have lost some of their flavour by drying out.

STORAGE AND PREPARATION
Store fresh ginger in a cool cupboard or the fridge. Some people say that this will make the ginger go mouldy, but I keep mine in the door and I've never had any problem. For longer storage, you can freeze it, but I don't really see the point.

To prepare root ginger, simply cut off the size that you need and peel using a sharp knife or peeler. Use a cutting board and very sharp knife. The rhizomes can be quite fibrous and woody if they are large or slightly dry. For finer grating I find my newly acquired microplane ideal, as with a normal grater your knuckles can get caught on the grater as well. If you have a guard on a fine grater you can simply put the ginger under the top part and shred efficiently, without damaging anything else.

Another way of getting grated ginger or ginger juice is to use a garlic crusher. It will need de-clogging several times, but this is the best way of extracting the oils and juice without the stringy bits.

SERVING SUGGESTIONS
Here is a brief list of ways to use fresh ginger:

- Chopped, puréed or grated with garlic and onion as a base for curries
- Slices steeped in boiling water for ginger tea
- Added to marinades for stir-fries with soy sauce and other spices, such as garlic, dry mustard, hot red pepper flakes or spring onions
- Added to pickles and chutneys
- Added to marmalades and jams for extra zing
- Added to otherwise fairly bland foods, such as lentils or yoghurt
- Making a 'ginger beer plant'
- Adding to cakes or icing
- Using in salad dressings
- Adding ginger and orange juice to sweet potatoes
- Adding grated ginger to baked apples

Powdered dry ginger or ground ginger should be kept in tightly sealed containers in a cool, dark place. It tends to be favoured for baking, although fresh ginger can be substituted for ground ginger. A suggested ratio is six parts fresh for every one part dried. Some cakes use both fresh and dried, although they taste quite different. Ground ginger is a poor substitute for fresh ginger in most cases. Ginger can be an acquired taste, so it is best to go gently at first when introducing it in a new recipe or cooking situation and then increase the amounts later. This is especially true of pickled ginger, which can be pretty eye-watering stuff and very salty. Another way is to store fresh ginger in sherry or Madeira in the fridge, using as much or as little as you want at a time.

Crystallised or stem ginger is good for cakes, ice cream and desserts. Since fresh ginger sours milk, it is the often used to infuse the flavour of ginger into ice creams, custards or creme brûlée.

Whatever sort you use, enjoy your ginger. Here are some ideas for trying throughout the day.
As always, metric and imperial measures are provided. There may be some discrepancy between equivalent amounts in different recipes, especially where quantities have been reduced or have been developed at different times. As long as you use either metric or imperial within any recipe there shouldn't be a problem.

WAKE-ME-UPS WITH GINGER

This section includes a healthy porridge recipe and some other goodies to start the day with.

OLD-FASHIONED BAKED PORRIDGE

I don't know how you'd manage this before work in the morning, although it would keep you going until lunchtime, with no bother!

Ingredients   **Serves 2**

  575 ml (1 pint) water

  ¼ teaspoon salt

  75 g (3 oz) medium oatmeal

  25 g (1 oz) raisins

  1 tablespoon maple syrup

  1 tablespoon black treacle

  1 tablespoon dark brown sugar

  1 tablespoon walnuts, chopped

  1 egg, beaten

  ¼ teaspoon cinnamon

  ¼ teaspoon ground ginger

  A pinch of nutmeg

  chilled milk or cream (optional)

Method

1. Preheat the oven to 180°C (350°F gas mark 4).
2. Bring the water to the boil, add salt, reduce heat and sprinkle in the oats. Cook for 5 minutes, stirring frequently. Transfer the oatmeal to an ovenproof dish.
3. Add all the remaining ingredients, except the milk or cream. Stir well.
4. Bake until set (approximately 40–45 minutes).
5. Spoon into bowls and serve with milk or cream.

BROONIE

Fine oatmeal gives this mild gingerbread a texture like wholemeal bread. Try eating it warm for breakfast, with butter or spread and marmalade.

Ingredients
175 g (6 oz) fine oatmeal

175 g (6 oz) plain flour

50 g (2 oz) butter or margarine

1 egg

1 teaspoon ground ginger

2 tablespoons treacle

1 teaspoon baking soda

150 ml (¼ pint) milk

Method
1. Sift the flour, ginger and baking soda and mix with the oatmeal.
2. Melt the butter or margarine with the treacle and add to the oat mix.
3. Stir well and add the egg, well beaten.
4. Gradually stir in the milk.
5. Pour into a greased loaf tin and bake at 200°C. (400°F, gas mark 6) for about an hour. It should be well risen and firm on top.

ORANGE PINEAPPLE SMOOTHIE

Ingredients   For each smoothie
110 ml (4 fl oz) orange juice

50 ml (2 fl oz) pineapple juice

½ banana

½ teaspoon grated fresh ginger

2 ice cubes

Method
Mix all ingredients in a blender or food processor until smooth.

GINGER PEACH SMOOTHIE

Ingredients   **Serves 4**
    240 ml (8 fl oz) boiling water
    1 small cube fresh ginger root, peeled and crushed
    2 tablespoons honey
    2 fresh peaches, peeled and chopped
    500 ml (1 pint) peach sorbet
    1 tablespoon lime juice

Directions
1. Put the ginger in the hot water with the honey and leave until cool.
2. Blend the peaches, sorbet and lime juice, then strain the ginger and honey water, adding to the blender.
3. Process until you have a smooth smoothie

MANGO GINGER SMOOTHIE

Ingredients   **Serves 2**
    1 mango, peeled and sliced
    3–4 ice cubes
    110ml (4 fl oz) low fat plain yoghurt
    110ml (4 fl oz) cold water
    3/4 teaspoons grated fresh ginger

Method
Mix all of the ingredients in a blender until smooth. Serve immediately.

Drinks

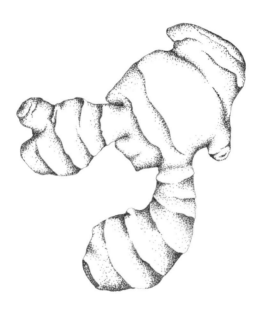

SOFT DRINKS AND BEVERAGES WITH GINGER

HOT GINGER COFFEE

You can use a coffee machine or filter and jug for this recipe. If using a jug method, use boiling water

Ingredients   **Serves 4**

> 6 tablespoons ground coffee
> 1 tablespoon grated orange peel
> 1 tablespoon chopped crystallised ginger
> ½ teaspoon ground cinnamon
> 1 litre water
> Whipped cream, cinnamon sticks optional

Method
1. Put the coffee, orange peel, ginger and cinnamon into a coffee filter. Brew the coffee.
2. Pour into mugs and garnish with whipped cream and cinnamon sticks.

HOME-MADE GINGER BEER

This is as close as I can find to the recipe we used when I was a kid. It was quite exciting watching the 'plant' grow and then brewing 'beer'. You need a very large container or brewing bucket for the second stage. This innocent little drink deserves a safety warning, in that bottles have been known to explode if left too long. You want the drink to be fizzy, but use plastic bottles which can be opened to release excess gas. If using glass bottles, don't put them directly on a cold floor and use corks, which can blow out rather than shattering the bottle. It's a lot of fun, really!

Ingredients

FOR THE PLANT

½ teaspoon dried yeast

1 teaspoon granulated sugar

1 teaspoon ground ginger

225 ml (8 fl oz) luke-warm water

TO FEED THE PLANT

7 teaspoons ginger

7 teaspoons sugar

FOR THE GINGER BEER

Juice of 4 lemons

675 g (1.5 lb) sugar

1.1 litres (2 pints) boiling water

2.7 litres (5 pints) cold water

Method

First, make the 'plant' as follows:

1. Put the yeast, ginger, sugar and lukewarm water into a clean jar. Cover with muslin and secure with a rubber band.

2. Feed this each day for seven days with one teaspoon of ginger and one of sugar.

3. Strain the plant through muslin or a clean tea towel into a bowl. Keep the gunge in the muslin, if you want to brew again. This should be divided into two and restarted in clean jars. You can give one jar away, if anyone else is willing to give it a go!

TO MAKE THE GINGER BEER

1. Place the lemon juice in a large bowl with the sugar and stir well.

2. Add the boiling water and stir until the sugar has dissolved.

3. Put in the cold water and add the strained juice from the plant and stir once more.

4. Leave the beer for a couple of hours and then pour into clean bottles and secure. Leave in a cool place for a week, when the ginger beer should be ready to enjoy.

ALCOHOLIC DRINKS WITH GINGER

I'm not a drinker of spirits, so most of the cocktails are included here for interest; just because they use ginger. Mulled wine is a different matter altogether, although it can be surprisingly potent. Please enjoy with care!

GINGER RUM COOLER

Ingredients   **Serves 1**

    50 ml (2 fl oz) dark rum
    175 ml (6 fl oz) ginger beer
    Wedge of lime
    Ice

Method
Fill a tall glass with ice. Add the rum and ginger beer. Stir and add the lime wedge.

GINGER MARTINI

Ingredients   **Serves 1**

    1 shot vodka
    ½ shot Amaretto
    1 shot honey syrup
    1–2 slices of fresh ginger
    Pinch of cinnamon
    Pinch of clove
    Piece of crystallised ginger to garnish

Method
Place the ingredients in a cocktail shaker or jar. Shake well, strain and serve with the ginger garnish.

MULLED RED WINE

The good thing about this is you can keep adding to it as the need arises. You don't need to use good wine either, as the other ingredients soften even the roughest red.

The addition of water means that everyone can enjoy it for longer, without getting pickled. I added Cointreau last year, but this is optional. The spices are essential.

Ingredients   **For 12 servings**

    2 bottles cheap red wine

    1.5 litres (2½ pints) water

    6 tablespoons honey

    1 stick cinnamon

    3 oranges

    2 lemons

    2 teaspoons grated fresh root ginger

    12 cloves

    2 tablespoons brandy or liqueur (optional)

Method
1. Stick the cloves into one of the oranges, all over the outside.
2. Put all the ingredients into a large saucepan and heat to simmering point. Don't let it boil.
3. Simmer for 20 minutes, stirring occasionally. Serve immediately (with a warning about the heat!).

Preserves
and
Pickles

CRYSTALLISED GINGER

I'm afraid I buy my crystallised ginger, since I don't use it a lot, but this recipe might prove of interest. It leaves a dry product, unlike the bought ginger in syrup.

Ingredients
>   500 g (1 lb) fresh ginger
>   225 ml (8 fl oz) boiling water
>   Cold water
>   225 g (8 oz) superfine sugar
>   450 g (15 oz) granulated sugar

Method

1. Peel the roots and cut into long narrow slices, across the grain.
2. Cover with cold water in a saucepan and bring to the boil. Simmer for 5 minutes, drain.
3. Repeat step 2, drain and dry well on kitchen paper.
4. Dissolve the granulated sugar in the boiling water. Boil for 10 minutes. Add the ginger slices and cook over a very low heat, this time without boiling.
5. Stir, and cook until all the syrup is absorbed. This will take about 40 minutes. Remove the ginger, and dry on a rack.
6. Roll the cooled ginger in superfine sugar, and let it stand in the sugar until it has crystallised.

PICKLED GINGER

Again, pickled ginger is quite easy to buy, but if you want to know the method, here it is. The ginger slices should turn a delicate pink colour. This is because of the anthocyanin, which turns pink when in contact with vinegar (*see Chapter 3*).

Ingredients

150 g (5 oz) young, fresh gingerroot

120 ml (5 fl oz) Japanese rice vinegar

50 ml (2 fl oz) water

1½ tablespoons sugar

Salt

Method

1. Peel the ginger and place it on a deep plate. Sprinkle with salt, cover and let it stand overnight.
2. The next day, rinse and pat dry. Cut it into very thin slices. Parboil these rapidly in boiling water. Drain thoroughly and place in a hot, sterilised jar.
3. Bring the rice vinegar, water and sugar to the boil in a small saucepan. Pour the mixture over the ginger slices, seal with a sterilised lid and let cool.

MANGO AND GINGER CHUTNEY

Ingredients

450 g (1 lb) mature green mangoes

1 small onion

50 g (2 oz) fresh ginger, peeled

1 clove garlic

300 g (11 oz) brown sugar

1 tablespoon chopped green chilli

½ teaspoon salt

225 ml (8 fl oz) vinegar

225 g (8 oz) currants

225 g (8 oz) raisins

Method

1. Coarsely chop the mangoes, onion, ginger and garlic. Add remaining ingredients and leave to stand overnight.
2. In a large pan, bring the mix to the boil, cooking rapidly until thick.

3. Pour into hot sterilised pint jars, and seal. Keep refrigerated once opened.

BEETROOT AND ONION CHUTNEY

This is a light, fresh-tasting chutney that's really easy to make.

Ingredients
> 100 g (4 oz) cooked beetroot in malt vinegar, drained and chopped
> 150 g (5 oz) onions, chopped
> 150 g (5 oz) cooking apples, peeled and chopped
> 2 tablespoons demerara sugar
> ½ teaspoon ground ginger
> 80 ml (3 fl oz) malt vinegar
> 1 teaspoon salt

Method
1. Mix all the ingredients together in a large saucepan. Bring to the boil and simmer gently, stirring occasionally, for 45 minutes.
2. Put into warmed, clean jars while still hot, and cover with jam jar lids or screw-on lids.
3. Store in a cool dark place until required.

PICCALILLI

Ingredients
> 225 g (8 oz) cauliflower florets
> 100 g (4 oz) French beans
> 100 g (4 oz) raw beetroot, peeled
> 225 g (8 oz) pickling onions
> 225 g (8 oz) diced cucumber
> 100 g (4 oz) salt
> 1 teaspoon turmeric
> 3 teaspoons dry mustard

½ teaspoon ground ginger

75 g (3 oz) sugar

430 ml (¾ pint) malt vinegar

4 teaspoons cornflour

Method

1. Put the vegetables, chopped and sliced, in a colander and add the salt. Leave to stand for as long as possible, then rinse and drain.

2. Mix the ginger, sugar, turmeric and mustard with a little of the vinegar. Add all but a few tablespoons of the remaining vinegar and put in a saucepan with the vegetables.

3. Simmer gently for about 5 minutes. Don't let the vegetables go soggy.

4. Mix the remaining vinegar with the cornflour, add to the pan with the vegetables and bring to the boil, stirring carefully.

5. After 3 minutes, spoon the mix into wide-necked jars, cool and cover.

APPLE GINGER JAM

Some recipes include crystallised ginger as well as fresh ginger, but I think there's enough ginger and sugar in this recipe already. An old saucer is useful to test the readiness of the jam and to preserve your worktops from damaging drips. If you've never made jam before, be assured that it can give you a very nasty scald and retains its heat for a long time, so be very careful.

Ingredients

225 g (8 oz) finely chopped fresh ginger

2 kilos (4 lb) apples

275 ml (10 fl oz) water

Approx 1.3 kilos (3 lb) sugar

1 teaspoon powdered ginger

Juice and zest of 2 lemons

Method

1. Peel, core and slice the apples. Put into a large deep pan with the fresh ginger and stir in the water.
2. Cover and cook until the apples are tender. Break them up with a potato masher. Measure the apple sauce produced.
3. For every 500 ml (pint) of sauce, add 350 g (12 oz) sugar and stir well until dissolved. Stir in the lemon and powdered ginger.
4. Bring back to the boil. Test for setting ability by removing from the heat and placing a little of the jam onto a saucer. If a skin starts to form immediately, it is ready. The pectin content will mean that this will happen quite quickly.
5. Cool a little before pouring carefully into sterilised jars. Cover and label.

Starters
and
Dressings

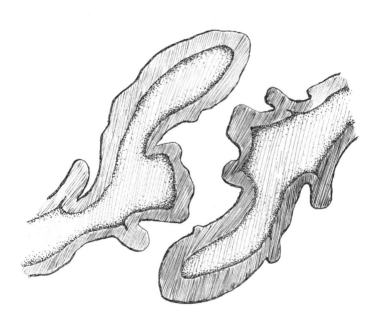

GRILLED SCALLOPS WITH GINGER

Because scallops are quite expensive we only usually have them in France, where we can buy them from the local fish market. You can use frozen ones, but I don't think they're a patch on fresh ones. Thaw thoroughly if you use frozen ones. I prefer to leave out the soy sauce as well. The cooking is important. If you overdo the grilling, they will be tough and rubbery.

Ingredients   **Serves 4**

   8–12 scallops, prepared and washed

   1 teaspoon grated fresh ginger

   2 tablespoons lime juice

   1 tablespoon olive oil

   1 teaspoon honey

   1 tablespoon soy sauce (optional)

Method

1. Put the lime juice, oil, honey and ginger in a bowl and mix well. Add soy sauce, if using.
2. Add the scallops and turn them to coat well. Cover and refrigerate for an hour.
3. Preheat the grill to hot. Remove the scallops from the bowl with a slotted spoon and place in a lightly oiled grill pan. Keep the marinade for basting.
4. Grill for about 3 minutes, turn and baste with marinade, and continue grilling for a further 2–3 minutes or until opaque throughout. Serve on a bed of salad leaves.

PUMPKIN SOUP WITH GINGER

I made this for an adult bonfire party last year. We sat in the garden and watched the firework displays all around us. The spicy kick given by the ginger was very well received, especially by one, confirmed carnivore friend, even though there was no meat involved. As a bonus, we used the pumpkin, one grown in the garden, as a lantern to drink the soup by, whilst some of the 'older boys' singed their clothes on the bonfire! You need a very large pan to accommodate all of the vegetables as they cook.

Ingredients   **Serves 6–8**

    1 kilo (2.2 lb) pumpkin or squash

    1 tablespoon grated root ginger

    2 carrots

    2 medium onions

    1–2 potatoes

    2 sticks celery

    2 teaspoons ground coriander

    1 teaspoon nutmeg

    2 tablespoons oil

    550 ml (1 pint) vegetable stock

    Juice of 1 fresh lemon

    Salt and pepper

    Crème fraiche to serve

Method

1. First prepare the pumpkin flesh by removing it from the shell and cutting into cubes. If you are carving the pumpkin, give yourself plenty of time.
2. Prepare the other vegetables and chop into slices.
3. Heat the oil and fry the ginger and other spices for a couple of minutes.
4. Add the chopped vegetables, cover and allow to 'sweat' for about 20 minutes.

5. Add half of the stock, half of the lemon juice, salt and pepper. Bring to the boil and simmer for about 30 minutes. Cool slightly.

6. Put through a food processor and add the rest of the stock and lemon juice. Reheat and check the seasoning. Serve with crème fraiche swirls in each bowl.

SALMON PARCELS WITH PICKLED GINGER

This is another favourite for special occasions, made even easier by using pickled sushi ginger. This can be bought from supermarkets in sachets. For a main course dish I use larger pieces of fish but the same amount of filo pastry. If you have time, marinade the fish in the ginger juice for an hour or two beforehand. If you are concerned about the added salt content, avoid this stage.

Ingredients   Serves 4

    2 x 125 g (4 oz) salmon fillets, skinned

    8 sheets filo pastry

    1 tablespoon chopped coriander

    1 tablespoon sushi ginger

    25 g (1 oz) butter, melted

    Grated zest and juice of ½ lime

Method

1. Preheat the oven to 190°C (375°F, gas mark 5).

2. In a small bowl, mix the lime zest, juice, sushi ginger and coriander. Place the fish portions in the marinade while you prepare the pastry.

3. Melt the butter in a small pan over a low heat. Brush a sheet of filo pastry with a little butter. Place a second sheet over the top and brush this with butter as well. Keep the rest of the pastry covered to stop it drying out and cracking.

4. Put a piece of salmon at one end of the pastry, with two or three slices of ginger and a quarter of the contents of the bowl of lime juice and coriander on top. Fold in the sides to keep the juices in and roll the parcel over until you get to the end. Seal carefully.
5. Repeat with the rest of the pastry to make three more parcels. Brush with any remaining butter and bake for about 15 minutes, until the pastry is brown but not burnt to a crisp. Don't be tempted to pierce the parcel to see if the fish is cooked, or you'll lose the juices. It'll be fine!

GINGER OMELETTE

Madame du Barry apparently delighted her clients with this dish, thought by some to have aphrodisiac qualities. Who knows? I'm writing this on Valentine's Day! If you want to be really cheesy, use the end of a spoon to write your initials in the egg as it cooks.

Ingredients   **Serves 2**

4 fresh eggs   salt and pepper
½ teaspoon fresh ginger   water

Method
1. Break the eggs into a large bowl. Fill half an eggshell with water twice, adding to the bowl with the ginger and seasoning.
2. Beat the mixture until fluffy.
3. Heat a lightly buttered frying pan and pour in the eggs. Cook until just done and transfer to a warm plate. Fold so that the initials (if made) are hidden.
4. Serve with hot rolls and butter and/or a salad of peaches and cherries (which were also thought to have special powers in the love department).

CINNAMON AND GINGER DRESSING

The easiest way to mix a dressing or marinade is to use a clean, screw-topped jar.

Ingredients
>   2.5 cm (1 in) fresh root ginger, grated
>   3 tablespoons olive oil
>   1 tablespoon white wine vinegar
>   1 teaspoon honey
>   ½ teaspoon ground cinnamon
>   Salt and black pepper

Method
Combine all the ingredients in a jar. Cover and shake well.

SWEET-AND-SOUR SAUCE

This base can be used for a variety of quick dishes.

Ingredients
>   100 ml (4 fl oz) honey
>   1 tablespoon cornflour
>   80 ml (3 fl oz) red wine vinegar
>   80 ml (3 fl oz) chicken stock
>   1 green pepper, finely chopped
>   1 tablespoon soy sauce
>   ¼ teaspoon crushed garlic
>   ¼ teaspoon ground ginger

Method
1. In a saucepan, combine the honey and cornflour.
2. Stir in the vinegar, chicken stock and the other ingredients. Simmer for a few minutes. Serve hot or cold.

Main Courses

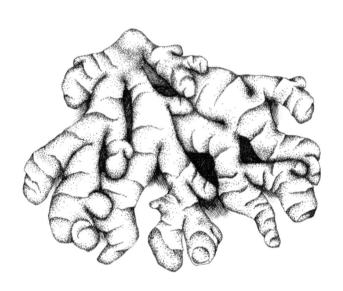

MAIN COURSES WITH GINGER

As you might expect, given that ginger originates from India and China, many of these recipes have an oriental feel about them. There is also a heavy influence from North Africa and the Mediterranean.

MARINATED LAMB WITH ROSEMARY AND GINGER

Using ginger wine makes a quick marinade for lamb or duck. You can use the same marinade as a sauce for roast duck (*see below*).

Ingredients   **Serves 6**

FOR THE MARINADE
    3 tablespoons ginger wine
    2 cloves garlic, crushed
    2 tablespoons olive oil
    Zest and juice of an orange
    Salt and pepper

    1.2 kg (2.6 lb) leg of lamb
    Sprigs of fresh rosemary

Method
1. Combine all the ingredients in a small bowl and mix well. Put the lamb in a roasting tin and pour over the marinade. Leave for an hour or two, spooning the marinade over the meat at intervals.
2. Preheat the oven to 200°C (400°F, gas mark 6).
3. Make slits in the lamb with a sharp knife and push sprigs of rosemary into the meat. Cover with foil and roast for an hour. Remove the foil and return to the oven for another 30 minutes. Serve with roasted carrots, potatoes and parsnips.

ROAST DUCK WITH GINGER

Use the marinade above (without the oil) and substitute bay leaves for the rosemary. Duck doesn't go as far as lamb, so this recipe will only serve four. You can use the duck fat removed from the cooking for roasting potatoes next time. Delicious!

Ingredients
Marinade as for roast lamb, but without the oil
1 x 2 kg (4½ lb) duck
8 bay leaves
Salt

Method
1. Preheat the oven to 200°C (400°F, gas mark 6).
2. Rub salt into the skin of the duck and on the inside. Put the bay leaves inside. Prick all over with a sharp fork. Brush with some of the marinade.
3. Place the duck on a trivet inside a roasting pan and cover with foil. Cook for 45 minutes and remove the foil. Drain off the juices but keep aside. Return to the oven for another 45 minutes. Let the duck rest before carving.
4. Fifteen minutes before the end of the cooking time add the rest of the marinade to the duck juices and heat in a saucepan. Simmer for 10 minutes and remove from the heat. Spoon off as much fat as possible from the sauce. Slice the duck and pour over the sauce to serve.

INDIAN LAMB

This is another firm family favourite. Preparation takes time, but the resulting taste is worth it in this wonderful mixture of spices.

Ingredients   Serves 4

3 large onions

5 cloves garlic

1 tablespoon grated fresh ginger

225 ml (8 fl oz) water

6 tablespoons vegetable oil

6 cardamom pods

6 whole cloves

Small piece of stick cinnamon

700 g (1.5 lb) cubed shoulder of lamb

2 teaspoons ground coriander

2 teaspoons ground cumin

Pinch of cayenne pepper

½ teaspoon salt

4–5 tablespoons plain yoghurt

Method

1. Cut two of the onions into fine half rings and chop the third one finely. Keep separate.
2. Put the garlic, ginger and a spoonful of water into a food processor and blend to a paste.
3. Heat the oil in a large pan and fry the sliced onions until brown. Remove from the pan and drain on kitchen paper. Put the whole spices into the oil and then enough meat to cover the base of the pan. Brown this meat, remove to a plate and add the rest of the meat to the pan to brown before removing.
4. Add the chopped onion, stirring until it turns brown. Add the ground spices and the garlic–ginger paste. Add the yoghurt, one spoon at a time, and stir with a wooden spoon.

5. Return all the meat and juices to the pan, with the water and salt. Cover and simmer for about 40 minutes. You can put it in the oven on a medium heat (190°C, 375°F, gas mark 5) if you prefer.

6. Just before serving, add the fried onions and check the seasoning.

SALMON IN GREEN GINGER SAUCE

These salmon steaks are grilled quickly and served with the green ginger sauce on top. This is a good barbecue recipe, as long as you don't overdo the grilling.

Ingredients   **Serves 4**

    4 salmon steaks

    2 tablespoons chopped parsley

    2 tablespoons chopped chives

    100 ml (4 fluid oz) olive oil

    1 tablespoon soy sauce

    2 tablespoons chopped onion

    2 tablespoons grated ginger

    2 tablespoons capers

    1 tablespoon lemon or lime juice

    Black pepper to taste

Method

1. Place the salmon steaks on a plate and brush with the soy sauce.

2. Blend the parsley, chives, onion, ginger and capers until smooth. Add the olive oil, pepper and lemon or lime juice. Mix well. Place the green sauce in a pan and simmer over a low heat while you cook the salmon.

3. Preheat the grill or barbecue. Cook the salmon steaks until just done. Serve with the hot green sauce.

CHICKEN AND STIR-FRIED NOODLES
WITH PICKLED GINGER

Here's a use for some of the sushi pickled ginger you might have left over from the salmon parcels in the starter section (*see page 128*).

Ingredients   Serves 4–6

   2 boneless, skinless chicken breasts

   3 tablespoons light soy sauce

   2 tablespoons rice vinegar

   1 tablespoon sesame oil

   1 carrot

   1 small green pepper

   2 tablespoons vegetable oil

   500 g (1 lb) spring cabbage

   1 clove garlic, crushed

   3–4 slices dried noodles

   2 tablespoons pickled ginger

   2 spring onions, thinly sliced

Method
1. Cut chicken lengthwise into 5 mm (¼ in) strips. Put these in a bowl with 1 tablespoonful of soy sauce, the rice vinegar and sesame oil. Leave to marinate for 30 minutes.
2. Meanwhile, thinly slice the carrot and green pepper into sticks. Prepare the spring cabbage by shredding finely.
3. In a wok or large pan, heat half of the vegetable oil. Stir-fry the chicken mixture in batches until it is browned. Remove to a clean bowl.
4. Add the rest of the oil to the wok and stir-fry the carrot, green pepper, cabbage and garlic for about two minutes. Add to the chicken.

5. Put the noodles with 175 ml (6 fl oz) water and the remaining soy sauce into the wok. Cover and steam for about 3 minutes.

6. Return the chicken mixture to the wok; stir-fry to heat through and make sure the chicken is fully cooked. Serve immediately.

CHINESE PRAWNS IN GARLIC SAUCE

This sounds like a lot of oil, but you only need to use it for deep frying the prawns. The rest of the food is then cooked in the residual oil left in the pan.

Ingredients   **Serves 3–4**

225 g (8 oz) peeled prawns

850 ml (30 fl oz) vegetable oil

1 teaspoon sesame oil

170 g (6 oz) sugar/mangetout peas

80 g (3 oz) sliced water chestnuts

50 g (2 oz) diced red pepper

25 g (1 oz) mushrooms

1 teaspoon chilli paste

1 teaspoon chopped root ginger

2 teaspoons fresh chopped garlic

FOR THE MARINADE/COATING:

½ teaspoon salt

½ teaspoon egg white

2 tablespoons cornflour

1 tablespoon oil

FOR THE GARLIC SAUCE MIXTURE:

1 tablespoon soy sauce

1 tablespoon sugar

1 tablespoon lemon juice

1 tablespoon white wine

1 tablespoon seafood stock or water

1½ teaspoons cornflour

Method

1. Wash and dry the prawns. Mix the ingredients for the marinade together, add the prawns and leave for about 2 hours in a refrigerator.

2. Meanwhile mix the garlic sauce ingredients together and leave to one side.

3. Heat a wok or frying pan over a high heat for at least 20 seconds and then add the oils.

4. Add the marinated prawns to the wok and cook for about 30 seconds, then remove the prawns and drain well. Pour the oil out into a bowl to cool.

5. Keep the residual oil in the wok, then add the chilli, ginger and garlic. Cook for 10 seconds. Add the garlic sauce mixture and cook until it thickens. Add the rest of the vegetables and cook for about 20 seconds over a high heat, until just cooked. Return the prawns to the wok and stir all ingredients thoroughly. Serve immediately.

CHICKEN WITH CITRUS AND GINGER

This Mediterranean dish probably originated in North Africa.

Ingredients   Serves 4

1 chicken, about 2 kg (4 lb)

2 lemons

2 oranges

3 tablespoons grated fresh ginger

Salt and pepper

5 tablespoons olive oil

2 tablespoons honey

Method

1. Preheat the oven to 190°C (375°F, gas mark 5).
2. Grate the zest from one of the oranges and one of the lemons, then squeeze out their juice. Cut the other lemon and orange into quarters. Rub the outside of the chicken with one of the lemon quarters.
3. Mix together the lemon and orange zests and 1 tablespoon of the grated ginger. Rub this mixture in the cavity of the chicken and place the lemon and orange quarters inside.
4. Place the chicken on a trivet in a roasting pan. Season with salt and pepper.
5. Mix the olive oil, lemon and orange juices, honey, and the remaining 2 tablespoons of ginger. Pour this over the chicken, cover with foil and roast for about an hour. Remove the foil, baste with the juices and return for another 30 minutes, or until the chicken juices are clear when you put a knife into a breast or thigh. Transfer to a plate and leave to rest before carving. Remove any fat from the juices, reheat and serve.

SPICY SPINACH WITH ONIONS

I love using spices in cooking. This dish is equally good with other spicy dishes or with roast chicken, and is an ideal way of using up a glut of spinach from the garden.

Ingredients   Serves 4

    1 kg (2 lb) spinach, washed and cut into strips
    110 g (4 oz) onions, finely chopped
    1 teaspoon fresh ginger, grated or finely chopped
    ½ hot green chilli (optional)
    4 tablespoons oil
    ½ teaspoon salt
    Pinch of sugar
    125 ml (4 fl oz) water

Method

1. Heat the oil in a large pan and stir in the onions. Add the spinach, ginger, salt, sugar and chilli. Stir and cook for about 5 minutes.

2. Add the water to the pan and cover tightly. Continue to cook over a very low heat for another five minutes.

3. Remove the lid and boil away any excess liquid before serving.

VEGETABLE CURRY

I have been using this recipe for about 20 years, both for vegetarian meals and as an accompaniment to meat dishes. It is easy to cook and very tasty. Just make sure that you don't overcook it, or you end up with a soup-like consistency, instead of crunchy vegetables.

Ingredients   Serves 4

1 small cauliflower

2 courgettes, sliced

2 onions, chopped

2 teaspoons chopped root ginger

2 cloves garlic, crushed

4 carrots, sliced

4 tablespoons vegetable oil

50 g (2 oz) cashew nuts

150 ml (5 fl oz) low fat plain yoghurt

2 teaspoons ground coriander

2 teaspoons cumin

2 teaspoons turmeric

225 ml (8 fl oz) vegetable stock

1 tablespoon fresh coriander to garnish

1 teaspoon garam masala (optional)

Salt and pepper

Method

1. Break the cauliflower into tiny florets and remove some of the stalk.

2. Heat the oil in a large pan and fry the onions until they start to turn brown.

3. Add the spices, garlic and ginger and then the carrots and courgettes. Stir and fry for a couple of minutes. Add the stock and cover the pan. Simmer for about 5 minutes.

4. Add the cauliflower and cook for another 5–8 minutes, or until the vegetables are still firm but edible.

5. Stir in the cashew nuts and yoghurt. Adjust the seasoning and if you want a bit more spice, sprinkle with garam masala. Garnish with coriander and serve with rice.

SPEEDY PRAWN CHOW MEIN

Make sure that the prawns are thawed properly, if using frozen ones.

Ingredients   **Serves 4**
- 2 teaspoons oil
- 1 large onion, chopped
- 2.4 cm (1 inch) root ginger, chopped
- 200 g (7 oz) fresh or frozen prawns
- 1/4 teaspoon Chinese five-spice powder
- 100 g (4 oz) fresh beansprouts
- Small tin sweetcorn
- 2 tablespoons oyster sauce or sherry
- 2 tablespoons light soy sauce
- 4 spring onions, sliced diagonally
- 225 g (8 oz) egg noodles

Method

1. Heat the oil in a wok or large frying pan. Stir-fry the onion and ginger for a couple of minutes.
2. Cook the noodles, following the instructions on the packet.
3. Add the prawns and five-spice powder to the wok and cook for a few minutes over medium heat. Stir in the beansprouts, sweetcorn, oyster sauce or sherry, soy sauce and the spring onions. Cook for a further few minutes.
4. Mix in the noodles, adjust the seasoning and serve.

Desserts

GINGER AND RHUBARB FOOL

Ingredients   Serves 4

    450 g (1 lb) rhubarb, sliced thinly

    1 tablespoon stem ginger, finely sliced

    1 tablespoon syrup from ginger jar

    Zest and juice of an orange

    1 stick cinnamon

    Ground cinnamon for garnish, or extra ginger slices

    150 ml (5 fl oz) double cream

Method

1. Place the prepared rhubarb in a saucepan with the cinnamon stick, ginger, syrup, orange juice and zest. Cover and cook for about 20 minutes. Cool completely and remove the cinnamon stick.

2. Whip the cream and fold into the rhubarb. Divide between serving bowls or glasses and chill for at least 30 minutes.

3. Garnish and serve.

UPSIDE-DOWN GINGER AND FRUIT PUDDING

This can be made ahead and stored in an airtight container for the flavours to mature. When you want to eat it just warm through and serve with custard, cream or crème fraiche. You could substitute pears or pineapple for the apple.

Ingredients

FOR THE BASE/TOPPING

    60 g (2 oz) soft margarine

    80 g (3 oz) brown sugar

    1 tablespoon fresh lemon juice

    2 cooking apples, peeled, cored and sliced

FOR THE STICKY GINGERBREAD

- 450 g (1 lb) plain flour
- 225 g (8 oz) dark brown sugar
- 175 g (6 oz) black treacle
- 175 g (6 oz) golden syrup
- 175 g (6 oz) margarine
- ½ teaspoon bicarbonate of soda
- 2 teaspoons baking powder
- 3 teaspoons ground ginger
- ½ teaspoon cinnamon
- 1 egg
- 225 ml (8 fl oz) warm milk

Method

1. Preheat the oven to 170°C (325°F, gas mark 3). Grease and line a baking tin or dish, approximately 30 x 20 x 5 cm (12 x 8 x 2 in).
2. Cream the butter and sugar together with the lemon juice for the base. Spread this evenly over the base of the pan. Arrange the sliced fruit on top.
3. Sift the flour, bicarbonate of soda, baking powder, cinnamon and ginger together into a large bowl.
4. In a saucepan gently warm the sugar, syrup, treacle and margarine.
5. Add the lightly beaten egg to the milk and pour these into the flour mix. Beat and combine with the syrup in the saucepan. Mix thoroughly.
6. Pour the batter over the fruit in the prepared tin and bake for 1 hour, or until firm. Leave the cake to cool in the tin for about 30 minutes, so that the fruit sets. Once completely cool, turn out of the tin and remove the paper.

GINGER ICE CREAM

This is a vanilla ice cream, with stem ginger for an exotic twist. It should come with a health warning!

Ingredients   **Serves 4–6**

4 pieces stem (crystallised) ginger, chopped
    into smaller pieces
25 g (1 oz) fresh ginger, sliced
2 tablespoons ginger syrup (from the stem ginger jar)
25 g (1 oz) caster sugar
2 teaspoons cornflour
3–4 drops vanilla extract
275 ml (10 fl oz) double cream
275 ml (10 fl oz) single cream
4 large egg yolks

Method
1. Whip the double cream until it holds its shape but is not too stiff. Leave to chill.
2. Beat together the egg yolks, sugar and cornflour in a bowl until smooth.
3. Pour the single cream into a saucepan with the fresh ginger slices and slowly bring to the boil. Simmer for a few minutes and then remove the ginger with a slotted spoon.
4. Pour the cream over the egg mixture and beat continuously. Return the custard to the pan and whisk over a medium heat until it has thickened.
5. Remove from the heat and return to a bowl. Cool in a larger bowl of water, stirring occasionally.
6. When cold, fold in the whipped cream, chopped ginger, syrup and vanilla. Pour into a plastic ice cream box, cover and freeze for 2 hours or so, until the ice cream has started to freeze around the edges.

7. Remove from the freezer and whisk to break up the ice crystals. Return to the freezer until required. Remove to the fridge about 30 minutes before serving so that you can scoop it out with a spoon.

8. Serve with extra stem ginger and syrup.

Variations
Along with the ginger, add to the cream ground cinnamon, ground nutmeg and ground cardamom to taste.

GINGER AND CINNAMON PEACHES

This is a quick and easy way to make a pudding out of ginger biscuits and tinned peaches.

Ingredients   **Serves 4**

50 g (2 oz) brown sugar

1 tablespoon lemon juice

1 teaspoon ground cinnamon

½ teaspoon ground ginger

1 large can sliced peaches in juice, drained

1 tablespoon melted margarine

225 g (8 oz) crushed gingersnaps

Low-fat yoghurt or crème fraiche (optional)

Method
1. Preheat the oven to 180°C (350°F, gas mark 4).

2. In a bowl mix together the sugar, lemon juice, cinnamon and ginger. Add the peaches and toss to coat them. Turn into a 20 cm (8 in) baking tin.

3. Mix the margarine with the ginger biscuit crumbs. Sprinkle over the peaches.

4. Bake for 25–30 minutes or until bubbly. Serve with low-fat yoghurt or crème fraiche.

GINGER CREAM ROLL

Here's another quick, old recipe with ginger nuts. With mandarin oranges, it reminds me of children's parties. It needs planning ahead to give the biscuits time to go soft.

Ingredients

225 g (8 oz) ginger biscuits
275 ml (10 fl oz) whipping or double cream
Mandarin oranges or stem ginger for decoration

Method

1. Whip half of the cream until stiff. Use it to sandwich the biscuits together in a long roll. Arrange on a plate and leave it in the fridge overnight.
2. To serve, whip the rest of the cream and cover the ginger roll. Decorate with mandarin oranges or stem ginger. Serve by cutting diagonally across the roll.

FRESH PINEAPPLE OR MANGO WITH PRESERVED GINGER

This is the easiest and quickest-made dessert going. It's a good standby for last minute preparation, but if you have time and want to look really flash, serve it in an ice bowl, like my friend Carolyn did. It's pretty impressive!

Ingredients   Serves 4–6

Slices or cubes of fresh pineapple
    or 2 fresh mangoes
2–3 pieces of whole stem ginger preserve
1–2 tablespoons syrup from the stem ginger jar

Method

1. Prepare the fruit by peeling and slicing into manageable pieces. Place them in a bowl.
2. Finely slice the stem ginger and stir into the fruit with the syrup.

HOW TO MAKE AN ICE BOWL

Once the ice bowl is made, you can be a bit canny and return it, rinsed, to the freezer as long as you don't dilly-dally over the pudding too long. Serve it on a large plate if indoors. We usually make these bowls for outside use on hot summer days.

You need

> 2 plastic bowls, one slightly larger than the other
> Sticky tape or masking tape
> Flower petals, lavender or leaves to decorate (optional)
> Water
> Patience!

Method

1. Get some long bits of sticky tape cut before you get your hands wet.
2. In a sink, fill the larger bowl half full with cold water. Put the smaller bowl inside this bowl and push down so that the rims are at the same level. This will allow some displaced water to run away into the sink. Remove from the sink and dry the outer bowl.
3. Now for the tricky bit; put the tape over the two rims and wind it over the tops. The idea is to keep the rims of the bowls in place whilst trapping water for freezing. If you've got an extra pair of hands, it helps, as the smaller bowl naturally wants to escape. It doesn't matter how rough the tape looks.
4. Put the leaves, petals or lavender into the water between the bowls and place in a freezer overnight.

5. To use, remove the bowls from the freezer and leave to stand for a few minutes, when the tape can be removed and the ice bowl liberated from between the plastic ones. Magic!

CHOCOLATE LYCHEES

Using cocktail sticks might help to dip the lychees and keep the chocolate off all the surfaces and your fingers.

Ingredients   **Makes about 20**
     1 large can (565 g) whole peeled lychees
     50 g (2 oz) crystallised ginger
     170 g (6 oz) dark chocolate
     1 tablespoon margarine

Method
1. Drain the lychees and dry them thoroughly on paper kitchen roll.
2. Cut the ginger into small pieces. Carefully stuff the lychees with the ginger.
3. Combine the chocolate and margarine in a small saucepan over a low heat, stirring constantly. After the chocolate has melted, remove it from the heat. Cool slightly.
4. Dip each stuffed lychee in the melted chocolate, making sure they are coated completely and evenly. You may have to dip each one more than once and build up layers. Place on wax paper to cool.

CHOCOLATE-DIPPED CRYSTALLISED GINGER

These would be delicious served with ice cream, or just as sweets on their own, with coffee.

Ingredients   **This makes lots of goodies**
    50 g (2 oz) good-quality dark chocolate, chopped
    40 or so pieces of crystallised ginger

Method
1. Melt the chocolate in a bowl over a saucepan of hot water.
2. Dip the ginger halfway into the chocolate. Arrange on waxed paper to set.

Cakes, Biscuits and Gingerbreads

CAKES, BISCUITS AND GINGERBREADS

Cake can't always be said to be good for you, but with the right ingredients it can deliver some of the foods that are good for everyone, regardless of dietary considerations. Cereals with slow release of energy, such as oats, go really well with spices like ginger and if you add honey into the equation, in moderation, you have another natural ingredient with health promoting properties. As a diabetic, I have to be careful about eating sensibly. That doesn't mean that I never eat cakes or biscuits, and if you look in any cookbook that is supposed to be for diabetics, you'll find these ingredients in use. You just have to be sensible with the amount of fat and sweeteners like sugar or honey.

BRANDY SNAPS

Ingredients
  50 g (2 oz) butter
  50 g (2 oz) brown sugar
  50 g (2 oz) golden syrup
  50 g (2 oz) plain flour
  2 pinches mixed spice
  ½ teaspoon ground ginger
  ½ tablespoon lemon juice

Method
1. Preheat the oven to 170°C (325°F, gas mark 3). Grease two baking trays.
2. Put the butter, sugar and syrup into a pan and heat until the butter melts and the sugar dissolves. Leave to cool.
3. Add the flour, mixed spice, ginger and lemon. Stir well.

4. Place teaspoonfuls on the baking tray with room to spread. Bake for about six minutes.

5. Leave to cool for a couple of minutes on the tray and then remove the brandy snaps, one at a time. Roll them round the handle of a wooden spoon and leave them to set. You can do this bit with two at a time. Serve with or without whipped cream.

PARKIN

This gingerbread-style, quite substantial cake hails from the north of England. Try eating it with cheese and apple.

Ingredients

120 g (4 oz) butter or margarine

120 g (4 oz) medium oatmeal

225 g (8 oz) porridge oats

120 g (4 oz) plain flour

3 teaspoons ground ginger

½ teaspoon bicarbonate of soda

¼ teaspoon baking powder

Pinch of salt

2 eggs

150 ml (¼ pint) molasses or treacle

1 tablespoon honey

80 ml (3 fl oz) milk

80 ml (3 fl oz) apple juice

Method

1. Grease and line a square 20 cm (8 in) baking tin. Preheat the oven to 170°C (325°F, gas mark 3).

2. Mix the flour, oats, salt, ginger, baking powder and bicarb together in a large bowl.

3. Put the butter/marg, molasses/treacle and honey in a saucepan and bring to the boil, stirring to mix.

4. Add to the dry ingredients and mix.

5. Put the milk, eggs and apple juice into the pan and heat gently. It may curdle, but don't worry.

6. Add this mix to the bowl, stir well and pour into the baking tin.

7. Bake for about 30–35 minutes. Cool and cut into squares.

GINGERBREAD

This old family favourite can be jazzed up with added fruit or nuts. It is easy to make and keeps fairly well. It is also good as a pudding, as my mother would have it, with custard or a drop of brandy.

Ingredients

225 g (8 oz) plain flour

1 teaspoon bicarbonate of soda

2 teaspoons ground ginger

150 g (5 oz) golden syrup

110 g (4 oz) margarine

50 g (2 oz) brown sugar

2 eggs

2 tablespoons milk

110 g (4 oz) sultanas (optional)

Method

1. Preheat the oven to 170°C (325°F, gas mark 3) and grease and line an 18 cm (7 in) square tin.

2. Sift the flour, bicarbonate of soda and ginger together in a bowl.

3. Warm the golden syrup in a saucepan with the margarine and brown sugar until the ingredients have melted. Add the milk and leave to cool.

4. Beat the eggs into the mixture in the saucepan and then mix this with the dry ingredients to form a thick batter. Stir in the sultanas.

5. Pour into the lined tin and bake for about 40–50 mins, or until cooked through.

TRULY GINGER CAKE

This is a ginger cake, through and through, with three kinds of ginger. Use a rectangular cake tin or roasting tin and cut into squares when cold. The icing can be tangy and spicy as well: lemon or ginger.

Ingredients

    4 pieces stem ginger, chopped finely

    2 tablespoons ginger syrup from the jar

    1 teaspoon ground ginger

    2 teaspoons grated fresh ginger

    175 g (6 oz) butter or margarine

    175 g (6 oz) golden caster sugar

    3 eggs, beaten

    1 tablespoon molasses or black treacle

    225 g (8 oz) self-raising flour

    2 tablespoons milk

FOR THE ICING

    50 ml (2 fl oz) lemon juice

    225 g (8 oz) icing sugar

    2 tablespoons boiling water

    OR

    200 g (7 oz) icing sugar

    75 ml (2 fl oz) ginger syrup

    75 g (3 oz) chopped stem ginger for decoration
        (optional)

Method

1. Pre-heat the oven to 170°C (325°F, gas mark 3). Grease and line a cake or roasting tin approximately 15 x 25 cm (6 x 10 in), leaving the paper above the edge of the tin.

2. Cream the fat and sugar until light. Gradually beat in the eggs.

3. Fold in the ginger syrup and molasses or treacle.

4. Sift the flour and ground ginger and fold into the cake gradually. Add the milk, grated ginger and stem ginger.

5. Turn into the tin and spread evenly. Bake for about 45 minutes or until springy to the touch.

6. Leave to cool in the tin a little and then turn onto a wire cooling rack.

TO ICE

1. Sift the icing sugar into a bowl and gradually mix in the lemon juice and water or ginger syrup. Don't add all of the liquid if the icing looks like it is getting too runny. Ice the cake when it is completely cold and leave to set.

2. Cut the extra ginger and place at equal intervals on the cake. Cut into squares or desired shape and serve.

GINGERBREAD PEOPLE

This method is slightly different and allows the gingerbread to chill so that it is easier to roll and cut

Ingredients   **Makes about 12**

    25 g (1 oz) butter or margarine

    50 g (2 oz) brown sugar

    110 g (4 oz) plain flour

    2 tablespoons golden syrup

    ½ teaspoon bicarbonate of soda

    ½ teaspoon ground cinnamon

    ½ teaspoon powdered ginger

    1 teaspoon milk

    Raisins for eyes and buttons, or ready made icing
        (optional)

Method

1. Sieve together the flour, bicarbonate of soda, ginger and cinnamon.

2. Heat the fat, syrup and sugar over a low heat, long enough to melt the sugar. Allow to cool.

3. Mix the dry and wet ingredients together with the milk to form a stiff dough. Put this in a plastic bag and chill for about half an hour.

4. Preheat the oven to 160°C (325°F, gas mark 3). Grease some baking trays.

5. Roll the dough out on a floured board, about 5mm (1/4 inch) thick. Using biscuit cutters, cut out the gingerbread people and place carefully on the baking tray. Collect up the off cuts and re-roll carefully. Add raisin eyes (optional).

6. Bake for 10–15 minutes or until firm. Cool on a wire tray and ice when cold.

HOW TO MAKE A 3D GINGERBREAD HOUSE

I once used the recipe for gingerbread people to make gingerbread houses with a groups of 7- and 8-year-olds (and a helpful parent). They caused great excitement and creativity with the decoration, which seemed to involve a lot of icing and sweets. You will need to double the ingredients at least.

You can be as creative as you like, as long as the gingerbread is hard enough to support the roof. So, perhaps the walls need to be a little thicker than for the gingerbread people. Use icing to 'cement' the sides together and decorate as flamboyantly as you (or the children) like.

Draw your templates on clean paper so that you can use them to cut the gingerbread to size.

For a basic gingerbread house you will need, as an example:

2 rectangles e.g. 15 x 10 cm (6 x 4 in)

2 rectangles e.g. 15 x 10 cm (6 x 4 in), but cut off triangles to form gables (*see template below*)

A roof made of two pieces approximately 17 x 10 cm (7 x 4 in).

TEMPLATE FOR GINGERBREAD HOUSE

ROOF PIECES X 2
17 cm x 10 cm (7 x 4 in) each

SIDE PIECES X 2
15 cm x 10 cm (6 x 4 in) each

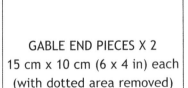

GABLE END PIECES X 2
15 cm x 10 cm (6 x 4 in) each
(with dotted area removed)